1 2 3 SUCCESS 2000™

D0246377

Millennium
COOKBOOK

Recipes low in Points...

Azmina Govindji

SIMON & SCHUSTER
A VIACOM COMPANY

Weight Watchers™

ACKNOWLEDGEMENTS

Several important people have helped me to put together this collection of recipes, by contributing both their own culinary skills and their discerning tastes when testing out the recipes. Elaine Gardner provided inspiring dishes like Curried Chicken Flan and Sweet And Sour Mushrooms. Marilyn Cunningham supplied traditional favourites such as Family Fish Pie and Lancashire Hot-pot. Sue Wrigley helped out with indulgent dishes such as Croissants Monsieur, and Cinnamon and Orange Scones, and Baldeesh Rai shared all sorts of culinary delights with us – Knickerbocker Glory and Baked Cheesy Triangles to name just two.

The Govindji family (kids included) have given their verdict on a whole range of original recipes. The most credit must go to my husband, Shamil, who always encourages me with my work and who supported me wholeheartedly in writing this book.

First published in Great Britain by Simon & Schuster UK Ltd, 2000
A Viacom Company

Copyright © 2000, Weight Watchers International, Inc.

Simon & Schuster UK Ltd
Africa House, 64–78 Kingsway, London WC2B 6AH

Photography: Steve Baxter
Styling: Marian Price
Food preparation: Carol Tennant

Text Design: Jane Humphrey
Typesetting: Stylize Digital Artwork
Printed and bound in Singapore

Weight Watchers Publications Manager: Elizabeth Egan
Weight Watchers Publications Assistant: Celia Whiston

A CIP catalogue record for this book is available from the British Library

ISBN 0 68486 013 9

Pictured on the front cover: *Chicken and Vegetable Kebabs; Pesto Haddock; Raspberries layered with Crème Fraîche and Filo Pastry; Prawn Puri; Chicken Tikka Masala; Gorgeous Gazpacho (left to right, top to bottom)*
Pictured on the back cover: *Cod Portuguese; 2-minute Trifle; Southern Fries (left to right)*

contents

Recipe Categories

These are Budget meals
Ideal for those of you on a budget or anyone trying to save a few pence.

These are Creative meals
Choose one of these recipes when you are entertaining or feel like trying something different.

These are Family meals
They are ideal for midweek suppers or for times when everyone wants some delicious and satisfying traditional fare.

These are Quick meals
Turn to these recipes after work or when you simply want to whip up a tasty meal in as little time as possible.

Recipe Notes

Egg size is medium, unless otherwise stated. Fruit and vegetables are medium-sized, unless otherwise stated.
It is important to use proper measuring spoons, not cutlery, for spoon measures.
1 tablespoon = 15 ml
1 teaspoon = 5 ml
Dried herbs can be substituted for fresh ones, but the flavour may not always be as good. Halve the fresh-herb quantity stated in the recipe.

Ⓥ shows the recipe is suitable for vegetarians

A new Millennium, a new way of eating and a new you!

If you're a Member of Weight Watchers then you'll know that the categories of recipes you'll find in this book – Budget, Creative, Family and Quick – are taken from the 123 Success 2000™ Programme. Based on various lifestyle themes, 123 Success 2000™ comes from the same family as our previous 123 Programmes. It works like this …

When you join Weight Watchers, your Leader will tell you how many Points you have available each day. All the food you eat is worth a certain number of Points, according to how many Calories and how much saturated fat it contains. As you spend your allocation of Points, you'll start to become aware that food which is high in saturated fat uses up more of your Points. This will encourage you to cut down on fatty food and go for low-Point versions instead. Bonus Points for exercise will encourage you to get moving – each activity is worth a certain number of bonus Points and you can spend these on extra food if you wish!

As well as following these basic guidelines, ensure your diet is healthy by eating a good variety of foods. Trying the new recipes in this cookbook will help you to do that. For example, you could make a new recipe each week. At that rate, there are enough recipes in this book to keep you going for several years. It's also important to fill up on fresh fruit and vegetables. The

Government health authorities recommend at least five portions a day. You'll find we've used lots of fruit and vegetables in these recipes. And if you're hungry, just add an extra serving of vegetables or salad to your plate.

Finally, do take a lively interest in food. We live in exciting times – air transport has meant that many exotic foods are becoming commonplace in our stores now. So, as well as eating in a healthy way, experiment freely. Flavourings, herbs and spices from all over the world will keep for a long time in your store cupboard. A dash or two of these can turn an ordinary dish into an exciting new taste discovery. So if a new jar, pack or bottle catches your eye, pick it up and read the label. And when you see a new ingredient in a recipe – buy it and try it. Healthy eating can be very exciting.

Enjoy what you eat!

introduction

Gone are the days when a weight-loss eating plan restricted you to boring and unadventurous foods. Crispbreads and lettuce leaves don't have to be regular menu items any more. Flick through these pages and you'll see recipes with a whole host of exciting flavours, all using simple ingredients available from your local supermarket.

This recipe collection includes something to suit all tastes and – perhaps more importantly – all types of cook. With this book, you don't need an exhaustive list of ingredients, nor do you need to be a dab hand in the kitchen. If you want to conjure up a speedy meal for four while making sure the children do their homework and putting a washing load into the machine, you'll find an array of dishes which you can have on the table in half an hour. And for times when you feel like experimenting with more exciting ingredients or showing off your talent in the kitchen, there are dishes like Beefsteak Romantica and Moroccan Chick-pea and Apricot Pilaff that will do just the trick.

So, enough reading! Let's rattle those pots and pans and get cooking!

You may feel you've seldom got time for the luxury of an appetiser, but here you'll find dishes that take less time than laying the table. All the recipes are in line with healthy eating principles and use low-fat, low-Calorie ingredients, so you'll be able to keep an eye on those Points while indulging in dishes like Seafood And Apple Cocktail or Prawn Toasties.

The recipes aren't elaborate and don't need fancy garnishes, but you might want to try sprinkling some chopped fresh parsley, coriander or spring onions on top, or maybe just add a swirl of low-fat plain yogurt or light evaporated milk to the soups. It's a good idea to scan the soup recipes. You'll find many use canned soup or canned vegetables as a basis, so have some of these handy in your store-cupboard for when you're stuck for ideas.

Many of these starters double up as satisfying main meals. Simply refer to the recipe introduction, or add a crusty roll to the soup dishes

So, if you have the odd 5 minutes and fancy adding a few frills to your meal, try the Gorgeous Gazpacho or the Barbecued Corn on the Cob.

soups

and starters

Barbecued Corn on the Cob

Ⓥ

1½ Points per serving

5½ Total Points per recipe

155 Calories per serving

④ Servings

Freezing not recommended. Preparation and cooking time: 10 minutes.

2 teaspoons runny honey
1 tablespoon Worcestershire sauce
1 tablespoon soy sauce
a good pinch of dried basil
a pinch of chilli powder
a few drops of sesame oil
4 medium frozen corn on the cob,
    cooked according to the packet
    instructions
low-fat cooking spray
freshly ground black pepper

1 Preheat the grill. Mix together the honey, Worcestershire sauce, soy sauce, basil, chilli powder, sesame oil and black pepper.
2 Spread this mixture evenly over each cooked corn on the cob.
3 Give each cob 4 sprays of low-fat cooking spray.
4 Grill for about 5 minutes, turning and basting frequently until the corn is golden brown. Serve immediately.

 Red Lentil and Carrot Soup

Ⓥ

3 Points per serving

5½ Total Points per recipe

225 Calories per serving

② Servings

Freezing recommended. Preparation and cooking time: 25 minutes.

1 teaspoon vegetable oil
1 small onion, chopped finely
2 carrots, diced
1 bay leaf
500 ml (18 fl oz) hot vegetable stock,
    made with a stock cube
100 g (3½ oz) red lentils, washed
2 tablespoons chopped fresh coriander
    leaves
1 teaspoon half-fat crème fraîche

1 Heat the oil and fry the onion, carrots and bay leaf for a few minutes.
2 Stir in the hot vegetable stock with the lentils. Return to the boil, cover and simmer for 10–15 minutes until the lentils are soft and mushy.
3 Stir well and mash the lentils a little with a large spoon. Add more hot water if necessary and mix in the coriander.
4 Pour into warmed bowls and top with crème fraîche.

Weight Watchers tip
To cut down on Points, omit the crème fraîche.

Thai Noodle Soup

Ⓥ

2 Points per serving

3½ Total Points per recipe

120 Calories per serving

② Servings

Freezing not recommended. Preparation and cooking time: 10 minutes.
Conjure up the aroma of the Orient in just 10 minutes – no one will guess you used a pack of instant noodles.

85 g packet of instant noodle soup mix
1 teaspoon sesame oil
1 teaspoon crushed ginger (see tip)
½ teaspoon dried basil
1 tablespoon fish sauce (or soy sauce)
175 g (6 oz) baby sweetcorn, drained
    and sliced
2 spring onions, sliced finely
freshly ground black pepper

1 Cook the soup according to the instructions on the packet.
2 Meanwhile, heat the oil in a pan large enough to hold the soup. Add the ginger, basil and fish sauce (or soy sauce). Stir in the sweetcorn and spring onions and season to taste with pepper.
3 Add the soup to the crunchy vegetables and heat through.

Cook's tip
Crushed ginger is available in jars or you can make it yourself with fresh root ginger.

 **Bits 'n' Dips**

V

3 Points per serving

5½ Total Points per recipe

170 Calories per serving

2 Servings

Freezing not recommended. Preparation time: 10 minutes.

This may seem like a long list of ingredients, but these dips are really speedy to make and great with all sorts of raw vegetables or with chips.

150 ml (5 fl oz) low-fat plain yogurt

5 cm (2-inch) piece of cucumber, grated and drained

¼ teaspoon dried mint

3 tablespoons tomato ketchup

3 tablespoons Worcestershire sauce

2 teaspoons soy sauce

1 tablespoon lemon juice

1 teaspoon runny honey

1 teaspoon mint sauce

½ teaspoon chilli powder

1 medium pitta bread, warmed and cut into strips

1 Mix together the yogurt, cucumber and dried mint and transfer to a serving bowl.

2 Mix together 1 tablespoon of tomato ketchup, the Worcestershire sauce, soy sauce, lemon juice and honey.

3 Add the remaining tomato ketchup to the mint sauce and chilli powder. Dilute with a little cold water so that it becomes quite a runny dip.

4 Serve the dips with strips of warmed pitta bread.

 **Florida Cocktail**

V

2½ Points per serving

10 Total Points per recipe

170 Calories per serving

4 Servings

Freezing not recommended. Preparation time: 10 minutes.

1 medium pink grapefruit, peeled and divided into segments

1 large orange, peeled and divided into segments

4 tablespoons canned pineapple chunks in natural juice, drained

175 g (6 oz) seedless grapes, halved

600 ml (1 pint) low-fat plain yogurt

1 Simply mix all the fruits together and add to the yogurt. Serve chilled. If you like you can serve the natural juice on the side.

 **Chicken and Sweetcorn Soup**

1 Point per serving

5 Total Points per recipe

110 Calories per serving

4 Servings

Freezing not recommended. Preparation and cooking time: 10 minutes.

400 g can Weight Watchers from Heinz chicken noodle soup

418 g can creamed sweetcorn

1 teaspoon cornflour

1 tablespoon light soy sauce

1 tablespoon chopped fresh coriander leaves (optional)

1 tablespoon chopped fresh parsley

2 tablespoons chopped spring onions

salt and ground white pepper

1 Heat the soup with the sweetcorn.

2 Make up a paste with the cornflour and 1 tablespoon of cold water

3 Add all the other ingredients and warm through. Season to taste and add some hot water if the soup is too thick for you.

Cook's tip

Do not boil, as this impairs the flavour.

 ## Stuffed Tomatoes

(V)

1 Point per serving
3½ Total Points per recipe
85 Calories per serving
4 Servings

Freezing not recommended. Preparation time: 15 minutes.
A great crunchy starter.

8 tomatoes, ripe but firm
200 g (7 oz) diet cottage cheese
1 crisp eating apple, diced, and drizzled
with a little lemon juice
salt and freshly ground black pepper

1 Cut the tops off the tomatoes and set aside. Scoop out the seeds from the tomatoes and discard. Season the insides with salt and freshly ground black pepper.
2 Mix together the cottage cheese and the diced apple.
3 Divide the mixture between the tomatoes, filling each one generously.
4 Place the tomato lids on top of the stuffing, pressing down gently to make the lids secure.

 ## Onion Soup

(V)

1 Point per serving
4 Total Points per recipe
85 Calories per serving
4 Servings

Freezing not recommended. Preparation and cooking time: 45 minutes.
There is something very satisfying about home-made soup. This soup makes an ideal starter for a dinner party.

350 g (12 oz) onions, sliced thinly
1 tablespoon vegetable oil
850 ml (1½ pints) beef stock
1 bay leaf
150 ml (¼ pint) red wine
salt and freshly ground black pepper

1 In a saucepan fry the onions in the oil for 10 minutes over a low heat.
2 Pour in the stock and bring to the boil. Add the bay leaf and the seasoning.
3 Cover and simmer for 10 minutes and then add the red wine. Continue to cook with the lid on for another 10 minutes.
4 Remove the bay leaf before serving.

Cook's tip
The soup can be prepared earlier in the day, allowed to cool and stored in the fridge.

Stuffed Green Peppers

(V)

2½ Points per serving
10 Total Points per recipe
215 Calories per serving
4 Servings

Freezing not recommended. Preparation and cooking time: 30 minutes.

4 green peppers
200 g (7 oz) easy-cook rice
5 spring onions, chopped finely
100 g (3½ oz) salsa sauce
salt and freshly ground black pepper

1 Simmer the peppers in boiling, salted water for 10–15 minutes. Drain thoroughly. Slice off the lids carefully and remove the core and seeds.
2 Meanwhile cook the rice according to the packet instructions.
3 Mix in the spring onions and season to taste.
4 Pile into the pepper cases and serve with the salsa sauce.

Variation
Add 100 g (3½ oz) chopped lean honey-roast or smoked ham to the rice. Remember to add ½ Point per serving and 70 Calories per serving.

Hot Roasted Vegetables

V

½ Point per serving

2½ Total Points per recipe

60 Calories per serving

4 Servings

Freezing not recommended. Preparation time: 10 minutes + 15 minutes cooking.

2 teaspoons olive oil
2 courgettes, sliced
1 red or yellow pepper, sliced
1 aubergine, sliced
2 tomatoes, halved and sliced

2 tablespoons balsamic vinegar
1 teaspoon honey
½ teaspoon dried basil
fresh basil, to garnish
a sprinkling of LoSalt and freshly ground black pepper

1 Preheat the grill. Line a baking tray or grill pan with foil and drizzle 1 teaspoon of oil over it.

2 Place all the vegetables in a single layer on the tray.

3 Drizzle the vegetables with the vinegar, honey and the remaining oil. Sprinkle over the dried basil and season with LoSalt and pepper. Grill under a medium heat for 15 minutes, turning frequently until the vegetables are softened and browned. Serve immediately, scattered with fresh basil.

Cook's tip

The salt substitute adds a distinctive flavour to the dish while helping you to cut down on salt, but use ordinary table salt if you prefer.

Hot Roasted Vegetables

Bean, Tomato and Pasta Soup

3½ Points per serving

15 Total Points per recipe

190 Calories per serving

4 Servings

Freezing not recommended. Preparation and cooking time: 30 minutes.
This hearty soup makes an extremely satisfying quick supper.

2 carrots, chopped roughly
1 tablespoon vegetable oil
600 ml (1 pint) vegetable stock
600 ml (1 pint) tomato juice
1 small onion, chopped
1 garlic clove, crushed
50 g (1¾ oz) dried mini pasta shapes
420 g can black-eyed beans, rinsed
*   and drained*
1 teaspoon dried thyme
25 g (1 oz) parmesan cheese, grated
salt and freshly ground black pepper

1 Fry the carrots in the oil for 5 minutes.
2 Add the vegetable stock, tomato juice, onion and garlic and bring to boil. Allow to simmer for 10 minutes.
3 Meanwhile cook the pasta according to the packet instructions. Drain.
4 Add the beans and thyme to the stock and simmer for a further 10 minutes.
5 Add the pasta and season to taste. Serve with the cheese sprinkled on top.

Variation
You can use any varieties of canned bean with the exception of baked beans.

Cauliflower with Mustard

1 Point per serving

4½ Total Points per recipe

100 Calories per serving

4 Servings

Freezing recommended only if fresh vegetables are used. Preparation and cooking time: 25 minutes.
A great dish with lots of crunch. It works equally well as a starter or as an accompaniment to a main meal.

2 tablespoons oil
2 teaspoons black mustard seeds
1 cauliflower, cut into florets
1 tablespoon dried mixed herbs
salt and freshly ground black pepper

1 Heat the oil in a wok or frying pan with a lid.
2 Add the mustard seeds and cook until they start to pop. This will only take a few seconds.
3 Add the cauliflower and cook, stirring, for about 5 minutes.
4 Add the mixed herbs, 4 tablespoons of water and some salt and pepper. Cover and cook for 10 minutes or until the cauliflower is tender but still has some crunch.

Variation
This works well with most fresh vegetables.

Tomato and Pear Soup

½ Point per serving

2 Total Points per recipe

60 Calories per serving

4 Servings

Freezing recommended. Preparation time: 15 minutes + 20 minutes cooking.
See if your friends and family can guess what is in this soup – its unusual, but delicious, taste will make them all wonder.

low-fat cooking spray
1 onion, chopped finely
400 g (14 oz) canned tomatoes with
*   herbs or 400 g (14 oz) canned*
*   tomatoes plus ¼ teaspoon dried*
*   mixed herbs*
410 g canned pears in natural juice
1 teaspoon dried tarragon
600 ml (1 pint) vegetable stock made
*   with a stock cube*
juice of 1 lemon
salt and freshly ground black pepper

1 Add 4 sprays of low-fat cooking spray to a non-stick saucepan and cook the onion until soft.
2 Add the rest of the ingredients. Cover and simmer gently for 20 minutes.
3 Liquidise to a smooth consistency. Check the seasoning and gently reheat if necessary.

Cook's tip
This soup is also excellent served chilled with some chopped fresh parsley.

Prawn Toasties

Weight Watchers tip

This recipe makes four large helpings but as the Points are so low, you can enjoy the treat. If you are serving the soup as part of a large celebration meal, divide it into six portions instead (40 Calories per serving).

Variation

Serve with a tablespoon of low-fat plain yogurt in the centre and some finely chopped chives instead of parsley. Points remain the same, but add 10 Calories per serving.

2½ Points per serving

11 Total Points per recipe

140 Calories per serving

4 Servings

Freezing not recommended. Preparation and cooking time: 20 minutes.

These toasts make delicious finger food and an ideal starter to serve before Szechuan Chicken with Green Pepper (page 80).

4 medium slices granary bread
100 g (3½ oz) peeled, ready-to-eat
*   prawns, chopped finely*
1 teaspoon sherry
1 teaspoon oyster sauce (optional)
150 g (5½ oz) cottage cheese
a pinch of salt
1 teaspoon sesame seeds (see tip)

1 Toast the bread on one side only.

2 Combine the prawns, sherry, oyster sauce, if used, cottage cheese and salt.

3 Spread the mixture on the untoasted side of the bread.

4 Sprinkle with the sesame seeds, if used.

5 Grill the toasties until they are heated through.

6 Cut each slice into 4 triangles and serve.

Weight Watchers tip

Prawn toasts in Chinese restaurants are usually deep fried. These toasties have all the crunch without the grease.

If you use sesame seeds the Calories are 160 per serving.

Prawn Toasties

 **Celery Boats**

½ Point per serving

½ Total Point per recipe

15 Calories per serving

4 Servings

Freezing not recommended. Preparation time: 10 minutes.
Serve as a starter or as a side dish. Quark is a type of fat-free cheese.

50 g (1¾ oz) Quark
4 celery sticks, cut into 4 cm (1½-inch) lengths
a pinch of paprika
freshly ground black pepper

1 Put the Quark in a bowl and season with pepper. Mix well.
2 Spoon a little of the Quark into the hollow of each celery stick.
3 Sprinkle the paprika over the Quark.

 **Kelly's Eye Soup**

1½ Points per serving

6½ Total Points per recipe

80 Calories per serving

4 Servings

Freezing not recommended. Preparation and cooking time: 5 minutes.
This soup is a wonderful standby for unexpected guests on a cold winter evening. They'll be amazed at the speed at which you produce this dish. You can use any brand of mulligatawny soup, but Heinz do a good one.

400 g (14 oz) canned mulligatawny soup
1½ cans Weight Watchers from Heinz Tomato Soup
4 tablespoons low-fat plain yogurt

1 Mix the two cans of soup in a saucepan and heat.
2 Pour into soup bowls and place 1 tablespoon of low-fat plain yogurt in the centre of each bowl to form the 'eye'.

Cook's tip
Don't boil the soup vigorously as this alters the flavour.

Variation
If you don't like spices, try oxtail or French onion soup instead of mulligatawny. Points per serving will be 1. Calories per serving are 85 for oxtail soup and 65 for French onion.

Exotic Dip

1 Point per serving

3½ Total Points per recipe

40 Calories per serving

4 Servings

Freezing not recommended. Preparation time: 10 minutes.
This fruity dip is delicious with celery and carrot sticks.

50 g (1¾ oz) half-fat crème fraîche
4 tablespoons low-fat plain yogurt
2 tablespoons crushed pineapple, drained
salt and freshly ground black pepper

1 Put the crème fraîche in a bowl, stir and mix in the yogurt.
2 Add the pineapple and some seasoning. Mix well.

Variation
Chopped and drained mandarin segments make a tasty alternative.

 **Pepper Dip**

Ⓥ

3 Points per serving

12½ Total Points per recipe

95 Calories per serving

4 Servings

Freezing not recommended. Preparation time: 5 minutes + 45 minutes cooking. Roasted vegetables have a wonderful, rich flavour. It's an ideal method of cooking for all sorts of vegetables such as courgettes, tomatoes and aubergine.

2 red peppers, de-seeded and
*   sliced thickly*
2 yellow peppers, de-seeded and
*   sliced thickly*
170 g tub yogurt and cucumber dip
*   with mint*

1 Preheat the oven to Gas Mark 7/220°C/ 425°F.

2 Place the sliced peppers on a non-stick oven tray. You don't need any oil.

3 Roast in the oven for 45 minutes.

4 Serve with the yogurt and cucumber dip with mint.

Cook's tip

Don't worry if the skin of the peppers goes black – this gives them a roasted flavour. If you're in a hurry, the peppers can be cooked under the grill for 10 minutes, but remember to turn them frequently and keep an eye on them as they can quickly become overcooked.

Mushroom Stack

Ⓥ

1 Point per serving

3 Total Points per recipe

60 Calories per serving

4 Servings

Freezing not recommended. Preparation time: 5 minutes + 30 minutes cooking.

4 large open-cup mushrooms, washed
*   and stalks removed*
a pinch of dried mixed herbs
1 beef tomato, cut into 4 slices
50 g (1¾ oz) half-fat Cheddar cheese,
*   grated*
mustard cress, to serve
salt and freshly ground black pepper

1 Preheat the oven to Gas Mark 5/190°C/ 375°F.

2 Put the mushrooms flat side up on a non-stick baking tray.

3 Sprinkle some mixed herbs and seasoning over the mushrooms and top with a tomato slice.

4 Bake in the oven for 25 minutes. Preheat the grill.

5 Sprinkle grated cheese over each mushroom and place under a hot grill until the cheese has melted. Sprinkle over the mustard cress and serve.

Cook's tip

Save the mushroom stalks to use in another recipe e.g. Tomato Rice (page 116). They taste just as good as the rest of the mushroom.

Weight Watchers tip

You don't need any oil as the moisture from the tomato slices keeps the mushrooms juicy.

Variations

Instead of the mixed herbs try sprinkling the mushrooms with a crushed garlic clove. You can also make mini mushroom stacks using closed-cup mushrooms and cherry tomatoes!

Barbecue Spare Ribs

2 Points per serving

7½ Total Points per recipe

130 Calories per serving

4 Servings

Freezing not recommended. Preparation time: 5 minutes + 1 hour marinating + 1 hour cooking.

Marinating meat gives it a lovely flavour and it's so simple. Let your fridge do all the work!

450 g (1 lb) pork spare ribs (4 ribs)

For the marinade

2 tablespoons tomato ketchup

2 teaspoons clear honey

2 tablespoons soy sauce

1 Trim any fat from the outside of the ribs.

2 In a shallow ovenproof dish mix together the ingredients for the marinade.

3 Add the ribs and spoon the marinade over them, covering them well.

4 Put the dish in the fridge and let the ribs marinate for at least 1 hour.

5 Preheat the oven to Gas Mark 1/140°C/ 275°F.

6 Bake the ribs uncovered in the oven for 1 hour. Turn once during this time.

Weight Watchers tip

Don't serve the marinade that is left after cooking. This contains the fat that has oozed out of the ribs.

Variation

If you want to hot things up you can add ¼ teaspoon chilli powder to the marinade.

Barbecue Spare Ribs

Asparagus Soup

V if using vegetable stock

1 Point per serving

4½ Total Points per recipe

110 Calories per serving

4 Servings

Freezing not recommended. Preparation
and cooking time: 10 minutes.
This soup has a delicate flavour.

4 medium slices crusty wholemeal bread
340 g canned chopped asparagus
300 ml (½ pint) chicken or vegetable
stock made with a stock cube
4 tablespoons 'runny' low-fat plain yogurt

1 Warm the bread in a low oven.
2 Liquidise the asparagus with its juices.
3 Combine the stock with the liquidised
asparagus.
4 Gently heat until hot. Do NOT boil.
5 Divide between 4 bowls and stir 1
tablespoon of yogurt into each bowl.
6 Serve with the bread.

Variations

If you want to make it meatier why not
add some chopped lean ham or leftover
chicken? – remember to watch the Points
though.

 ## Tattie, Leek and Smoked Haddock Chowder

1½ Points per serving

7 Total Points per recipe

160 Calories per serving

4 Servings

Freezing recommended. Preparation time:
10 minutes + 20 minutes cooking.
This is a hearty and filling soup, ideal for
a chilly winter's night, and so simple to
make. If you don't have a blender or food
processor, don't worry, the soup will taste
just as good, but it will be chunkier.

850 ml (1½ pints) vegetable stock, either
fresh or made from 2 Knorr cubes
225 g (8 oz) leeks (fresh or frozen),
sliced thinly
350 g (12 oz) potatoes, peeled and cut
into small cubes
150 ml (¼ pint) semi-skimmed milk
225 g (8 oz) smoked haddock, cut into
bite-size pieces
2 tablespoons chopped fresh parsley or
chives (optional)
white pepper

1 Bring the stock to a simmer.
2 Simmer the leeks and potatoes in the
stock for 15 minutes.
3 Remove from the heat and add the milk.
4 Transfer the liquid with half the leek and
potato to a blender or food processor, and
whizz for a few seconds until thickened.
5 Return the blended and unblended soup
to the pan, add the smoked haddock and
cook for a further 5 minutes.

6 Season with white pepper and sprinkle
with chopped fresh parsley or chives, if
used, before serving.

Variation

Omit the fish and serve chilled for a
delicious vegetarian summer starter.
The Calories will be reduced to 110
per serving, Points to 1 per serving.

Gorgeous Gazpacho

V

1 Point per serving

4½ Total Points per recipe

95 Calories per serving

4 Servings

Freezing recommended without the croûtons.
Preparation time: 15 minutes + 1 hour
chilling.

Traditionally this Spanish soup includes
olive oil and vinegar. Our version is equally
delicious, but lower in Calories and
absolutely fat-free! Better still, if you have
a blender or food processor, it can be
prepared in about 5 minutes – just chop
the ingredients coarsely and whizz together
for a few seconds before chilling.

1 litre (1¾ pints) good-quality
  tomato juice
½ red pepper, de-seeded and
  chopped finely
½ green pepper, de-seeded and
  chopped finely
5 cm (2-inch) piece cucumber,
  chopped finely
½ onion, chopped finely
½ teaspoon garlic powder
1 teaspoon caster sugar
salt and freshly ground black pepper

To serve

2 medium slices bread, toasted and
  cut into croûtons

1 Mix together the tomato juice, peppers,
cucumber, onion and garlic powder, or
whizz in a blender or food processor for a
few seconds till thick but still crunchy.

2 Season with salt and pepper and stir in
the sugar.

3 Chill for at least 1 hour before serving
with the croûtons.

Cook's tips

Del Monte is a particularly good brand of
tomato juice.

If you use a blender or food processor
and the soup is too thick for your taste,
thin it out with more tomato juice, or a
little water.

For a special occasion serve little bowls
of finely chopped tomato, red and green
pepper and cucumber for your guests to
sprinkle on the soup with the croûtons.

Variations

If you want to serve the traditional version
of this soup, whisk in 2 tablespoons each
of olive oil and vinegar just before serving.
But, remember, this will add an extra
1 Point (and an extra 65 Calories) per
serving.

To serve hot, leave out the cucumber
and cook the other vegetables in
simmering tomato juice for 5 minutes.

Multi Melon Cocktail

1 Point per serving

3 Total Points per recipe

40 Calories per serving

4 Servings

Freezing not recommended. Preparation time: 30 minutes.

The mint in this cocktail is just so refreshing, and the different colours of the melon make it very pretty. It's so low in Points you can indulge with a clear conscience.

½ medium Galia melon

1 medium slice watermelon

¼ canteloupe or honeydew melon

1 lime

1 tablespoon chopped fresh mint leaves

a few sprigs of mint

1 Scoop balls out of the three melons (see tip) and mix the balls together in a large bowl.

2 Finely grate the zest of the lime and squeeze the juice.

3 Pour this over the melon. Mix in the chopped mint.

4 Serve in wine glasses or sundae dishes and garnish with a sprig of mint.

Cook's tip

There is a special tool for making melon balls, but a 10 ml spoon from a set of round measuring spoons can be used instead.

Seafood and Apple Cocktail

5 Points per serving

20 Total Points per recipe

155 Calories per serving

4 Servings

Freezing not recommended. Preparation time: 10 minutes + 1 hour defrosting.

A great starter to a special meal. This is a variation on the old 70s favourite, prawn cocktail. The seafood sticks and apple add refreshing flavour and bite, and – better still – you save on those all-too-expensive prawns.

175 g (6 oz) Cox's apple, peeled, cored and diced

2 teaspoons lemon juice

crisp lettuce leaves, shredded

225 g (8 oz) cooked, peeled prawns, defrosted

8 seafood sticks, defrosted and chopped

8 tablespoons Weight Watchers from Heinz 90% fat-free mayonnaise

2 tablespoons tomato ketchup

a dash of Tabasco or other hot pepper sauce

salt and freshly ground black pepper

To garnish

4 wedges of lemon and/or 4 whole unshelled prawns

1 Toss the apple in the lemon juice.

2 Line four serving glasses or individual dishes with lettuce.

3 Mix the prawns with the seafood sticks, apple and juice.

4 Mix together the mayonnaise, tomato ketchup and Tabasco or pepper sauce and combine with the prawn mixture. Season to taste.

5 Divide between the glasses or dishes and garnish with a wedge of lemon and/or a whole unshelled prawn.

Cook's tip

The seafood and apple mixture can be made ahead of time and kept in the fridge until required, but the cocktails should be assembled just before serving to prevent the lettuce from going soggy.

Weight Watchers tip

If you want to cut the Points even more, use a fat-free Thousand Island dressing instead of the mayonnaise. This will reduce the Points by 1 per serving. Calories will be 145 per serving.

Stuffed Eggs

2½ Points per serving

10 Total Points per recipe

135 Calories per serving

4 Servings

Freezing not recommended. Preparation time: 20 minutes.

4 eggs, hard-boiled
60 g (2 oz) low-fat soft cheese
2–3 drops of Tabasco sauce
½ teaspoon paprika
3–4 capers, chopped
salt and freshly ground black pepper
For the salad
mixed salad leaves, e.g., Little Gem,
  Lollo Rosso, radicchio, oak-leaf
  lettuce, etc.
2 teaspoons walnut or vegetable oil
4 teaspoons red wine or light malt
  vinegar
1 teaspoon chopped red pepper
sprigs of fresh dill or parsley, to garnish

1 Shell the eggs and carefully halve them lengthways. Scoop out the yolks and place them in a small bowl. Mash them with a fork.

2 Add the soft cheese to the egg yolks and mix well. Blend in the Tabasco sauce, paprika and capers. Season with a little salt and pepper. Spoon this mixture back into the empty whites.

3 Arrange the mixed salad leaves on four serving plates. Mix together the oil and vinegar and season with salt and pepper. Sprinkle over the lettuce.

4 Position the stuffed eggs on top of the salad leaves and decorate with a little chopped red pepper and sprigs of fresh dill or parsley.

The recipes in this chapter are really worth getting to know. They're all about minimum effort, maximum taste. A lot of the foods that we fancy when we're watching our weight are to be found here, but in fabulous low-Points versions that will really help you stick to your eating plan. Just take a look at dishes such as Speedy Pizza, Sweet and Sour Beans with Chips, Bangers 'n' Mash and Honeyed Chicken Drumsticks.

light
meals

Sweet and Sour Beans with Chips

V

2 Points per serving

7½ Total Points per recipe

175 Calories per serving

4 Servings

Freezing not recommended. Preparation and cooking time: 15 minutes.
A fresh alternative to a family favourite.

300 g (10½ oz) Healthy Eating oven
chips
½–1 teaspoon chilli powder
420 g Weight Watchers from Heinz
Baked Beans
2 teaspoons lemon juice
1 tablespoon soy sauce
sprinkling of LoSalt

1 Preheat the grill to medium hot. Line the grill pan with foil.
2 Place the frozen chips in one layer on the grill pan and sprinkle with LoSalt and chilli powder. Cook for 10–12 minutes, turning once during cooking.
3 Meanwhile, heat the baked beans and add the lemon juice and soy sauce. Serve with the chips.

Chick-pea Pitta Pockets

V

4 Points per serving

15½ Total Points per recipe

200 Calories per serving

4 Servings

Freezing not recommended. Preparation and cooking time: 20 minutes.

1 tablespoon olive oil
1 teaspoon cumin seeds
1 teaspoon mustard seeds
2 garlic cloves, crushed, or 2 teaspoons
garlic purée
½ teaspoon ginger purée
200 g (7 oz) canned chopped tomatoes
¼ teaspoon chilli powder
400 g (14 oz) canned chick-peas, drained
salt

To serve
2 white or wholemeal medium pitta breads
shredded lettuce

1 Heat the oil in a heavy based non-stick pan or cast-iron balti dish. Add the cumin seeds, mustard seeds, garlic and ginger and stir-fry for 1–2 minutes. The seeds will pop, so cover with a lid.
2 Add the tomatoes and chilli powder and cook over a low heat for about 5 minutes. Add the drained chick-peas, stir and simmer for 8–10 minutes. Check halfway through cooking and add a little water if the mixture starts to stick.
3 Warm the pitta breads in a low oven. Halve and fill with shredded lettuce.
4 Season the chick-peas and serve, hot or cold, stuffed into pitta breads.

Honeyed Chicken Drumsticks

2½ Points per serving

9½ Total Points per recipe

180 Calories per serving

4 Servings

Freezing not recommended. Preparation time: 10 minutes + 30 minutes cooking.

4 medium chicken drumsticks, skinned
2 tablespoons runny honey
1 tablespoon sesame oil
3 tablespoons soy sauce
2 tablespoons lemon juice
2 teaspoons coarse-grain mustard
salt and freshly ground black pepper

1 Preheat the oven to Gas Mark 6/200°C/ 400°F. Pierce the drumsticks with a skewer or fork to allow the flavours to penetrate.
2 Mix together the honey, sesame oil, soy sauce, lemon juice, and coarse-grain mustard. Place the chicken in a lightly greased ovenproof dish and spread this mixture evenly over the chicken. Season to taste.
3 Cook for 25–30 minutes till the juices run clear when you pierce the chicken with a fork. Serve hot or cold.

Bangers 'n' Mash

7½ Points per serving

30 Total Points per recipe

335 Calories per serving

4 Servings

Freezing not recommended. Preparation and cooking time: 20 minutes.
This typical British dish is usually high in fat from the sausages and the butter in the mash. Create this version using lower-fat alternatives. If you prefer a non-meat option, simply go for a pack of veggie sausages.

This recipe also includes a short-cut alternative to onion gravy by cooking the onion with the potatoes and then using instant gravy.

450 g (1 lb) potatoes, chopped
1 onion, finely chopped
150 ml (¼ pint) skimmed milk
4 teaspoons half-fat butter
4 teaspoons instant gravy granules
450 g (1 lb) reduced-fat sausages, grilled
salt and white pepper

1 Boil the potatoes with the onion until soft. Drain and mash with the milk, butter and seasoning.
2 Make up the gravy according to the packet instructions.
3 Grill the sausages and serve with the gravy and the mash.

Bangers 'n' Mash

Sky-high Turkey

3 Points per serving with yogurt

5½ Points per serving with fromage frais

205 Calories per serving with yogurt or 0% fat fromage frais

255 Calories with 8% fat fromage frais

1 Serving

Freezing not recommended. Preparation time: 10 minutes.

Turkey is a low-fat meat, and when you use wafer-thin slices, you'll find the sky's the limit! This open sandwich allows you to go as high as you dare, since the salad veggies are all free from Points.

1 medium slice bread, toasted
3 Iceberg lettuce leaves
1 tomato, sliced
2.5 cm (1-inch) piece of cucumber, sliced
6 slices wafer-thin smoked turkey
3 tablespoons low-fat plain yogurt or fromage frais
1 teaspoon coarse-grain mustard
freshly ground black pepper

1 Top the toast with layers of vegetables and turkey.
2 Make a dressing with the yogurt or fromage frais, mustard and pepper. Drizzle the dressing generously over the sandwich.

 **Cheat's BLT**

4 Points per serving

295 Calories per serving

1 Serving

Freezing not recommended. Preparation and cooking time: 10 minutes.
Standard bacon, lettuce and tomato sandwiches are often high in Points, especially if the bacon is cooked in fat – as it often is in cafes. Try this healthier alternative which uses turkey rashers instead.

4 medium turkey rashers
2 crisp lettuce leaves
2 medium slices wholemeal bread, lightly toasted
1 tomato, sliced
2 teaspoons tomato ketchup
a dollop of French mustard

1 Grill or dry-fry the turkey rashers according to the instructions on the packet.
2 Place the lettuce on a slice of toast. Top with the turkey and sliced tomato. Add the ketchup and mustard. Put the other slice of bread on top and serve immediately.

Variation
Use meat-free rashers for a vegetarian option. Adjust Points if necessary.

 **Fish Submarine**

5 Points per serving

260 Calories per serving

1 Serving

Freezing not recommended. Preparation and cooking time: 15 minutes.
This recipe reminds me of the first time I went to America – until then I never knew that a submarine was another name for a large finger roll sandwich. This filling is great for kids who could eat fish fingers and chips every day, and it's useful for days when you haven't got time to sit with a knife and fork.

2 fish fingers, grilled
1 tomato, sliced
2 crisp lettuce leaves
1 small low-fat cheese slice
1 finger roll, slit open
2 teaspoons tomato ketchup

1 Layer the fish fingers, tomato, lettuce and cheese on one side of the finger roll.
2 Spoon on the ketchup. Top with the other half of the roll and serve immediately.

 ## Spicy Potatoes

Ⓥ

3½ Points per serving

13½ Total Points per recipe

250 Calories per serving

4 Servings

Freezing recommended. Preparation and cooking time: 25 minutes.

These tangy potatoes taste delicious with Cucumber Raita (page 68) and warmed pitta bread. Remember to add on the extra Points.

750 g (1 lb 10 oz) potatoes, halved or
*   quartered*
2 tablespoons vegetable oil
½ teaspoon mustard seeds
1 garlic clove, crushed
200 ml (7 fl oz) passata
1 teaspoon curry powder
salt

1 Boil the potatoes for in salted water for 5–7 minutes until half cooked. Then drain. When the potatoes are cool enough to handle cut them into bite-sized pieces.

2 Heat the oil in a non-stick pan and add the mustard seeds and garlic. Fry them together, stirring, until the garlic is slightly browned.

3 Add the passata and the curry powder. Simmer for 2 minutes.

4 Add the potatoes to the sauce, and cover and cook over a low heat until the potatoes are completely cooked, stirring occasionally. Check seasoning before serving.

 ## Pasta in Cream and Mustard Sauce

Ⓥ

5½ Points per serving

22½ Total Points per recipe

345 Calories per serving

4 Servings

Freezing recommended. Preparation and cooking time: 25 minutes.

250 g (9 oz) pasta spirals
2 teaspoons corn oil
1 onion, chopped roughly
1 teaspoon crushed garlic
175 g (6 oz) half-fat crème fraîche
2 teaspoons coarse-grain mustard
½ teaspoon dried oregano
1 tablespoon chopped fresh parsley
LoSalt to taste

1 Boil the pasta according to the packet instructions, using LoSalt or, if you prefer, table salt.

2 Heat the oil and fry the onion and garlic for about 3–4 minutes.

3 Stir in the crème fraîche, mustard, oregano and seasoning.

4 Add the pasta and stir in the parsley. Warm through and serve.

Variation

You can use any dried or fresh pasta for this recipe. It also makes a good base for canned tuna.

 **Speedy Pizza**

V

3½ Points per serving

14 Total Points per recipe

280 Calories per serving

4 Servings

Freezing not recommended. Preparation and cooking time: 30 minutes.
As the name suggests, this is a quick light meal and a favourite with the kids.

1 tablespoon vegetable oil
1 onion, chopped finely
1 garlic clove, crushed
50 g (1¾ oz) mushrooms, sliced
1 green pepper, de-seeded and chopped
425 g (15 oz) canned tomatoes
1 teaspoon dried mixed herbs
1 small french loaf, halved horizontally
  and each half cut in two
75 g (2¾ oz) grated half-fat Cheddar
  cheese
salt and freshly ground black pepper

1 Heat the oil in a pan and cook the onion and the garlic until soft.
2 Add the mushrooms and pepper, and then the tomatoes. Boil until the tomatoes are reduced and thickened.
3 Add the herbs and seasoning.
4 Spread the mixture over the bread. Sprinkle with the grated cheese.
5 Preheat the grill to medium. Grill the bread until the cheese has melted and the pizza is hot all the way through.

 **Baked Cheesy Triangles**

V

4 Points per serving

15½ Total Points per recipe

260 Calories per serving

4 Servings

Freezing not recommended. Preparation and cooking time: 25 minutes.
Quick cheese on toast can be made quite memorable with a few tasty additions. Serve these cheesy triangles with a simple salad of lettuce and cherry tomatoes.

8 medium slices bread, with crusts
  removed
100 g (3½ oz) half-fat Cheddar cheese,
  grated
1 egg, beaten
150 ml (¼ pint) semi-skimmed milk
a pinch of pepper

1 Preheat the oven to Gas Mark 4/180°C/ 350°F.
2 Cover 4 bread slices with the cheese. Top with the remaining slices.
3 Cut each sandwich into 4 triangles and place in a shallow ovenproof dish.
4 Whisk the egg and the milk together with a pinch of pepper.
5 Pour this mixture over the sandwiches and bake for 15 minutes.

Cook's tip
This is best served at once.

 **Tuna with Mixed Vegetables**

2½ Points per serving

10 Total Points per recipe

185 Calories per serving

4 Servings

Freezing not recommended. Preparation and cooking time: 20 minutes.
This is a quick, low-fat, nutritious dish conjured up in under 20 minutes. Serve at once with rice or pasta, or as a filling for jacket potatoes or pitta breads. Remember to add the extra Points.

2 teaspoons vegetable oil
1 garlic clove, crushed
400 g (14 oz) can chopped tomatoes
125 ml (4 fl oz) smooth tomato juice
125 g (4½ oz) frozen sweetcorn
125 g (4½ oz) frozen peas
150 g (5½ oz) can red kidney beans,
  drained
1 teaspoon dried mixed herbs
175 g (6 oz) can tuna chunks in water,
  drained
6 spring onions, sliced
salt and freshly ground black pepper

1 Heat the oil in a pan and gently fry the garlic.
2 Stir in the tomatoes, tomato juice, sweetcorn, peas and beans.
3 Season to taste, add the herbs and bring to the boil. Simmer for 5 minutes.
4 Add the tuna to the sauce and heat through gently.
5 Stir in the spring onions just before serving.

Quick Goulash

 Pasta with Crabmeat

 **Spicy Burgers**

(V)

3½ Points per serving

14½ Total Points per recipe

230 Calories per serving

4 Servings

Freezing not recommended. Preparation and cooking time: 25 minutes.

If you're in a hurry, this makes a satisfying meal in less than half an hour. Serve with bread, boiled rice, pitta bread, or jacket potatoes. Remember to add the extra Points.

2 teaspoons vegetable oil

1 onion, chopped finely

1 garlic clove, crushed

1 teaspoon cumin seeds

2 courgettes, diced

2 teaspoons paprika

420 g canned tomatoes

2 × 400 g (14 oz) can of mixed beans,
    rinsed and drained

Lo-salt

2 tablespoons low-fat plain yogurt

1 Heat the oil and fry the onion, garlic, cumin seeds and courgettes for 5 minutes until the onions are lightly browned.

2 Stir in the paprika and pour in the tomatoes and beans. Season with Lo-salt. Cover and simmer for 15 minutes.

3 Drizzle on the yogurt just before serving.

Weight Watchers tip

Beans are an excellent source of fibre, they're low in Calories and very satisfying.

5½ Points per serving

23 Total Points per recipe

415 Calories per serving

4 Servings

Freezing not recommended. Preparation and cooking time: 20 minutes.

Crabmeat can be quite bland eaten on its own, but this recipe combines it with garlic and mushrooms to make a tasty, speedy dish.

2 tablespoons vegetable oil

1 red onion, chopped

2 garlic cloves, crushed

100 g (3½ oz) button mushrooms

340 g bottle passata

300 g (10½ oz) pasta, e.g. penne

210 g crabmeat in brine, drained

salt and freshly ground black pepper

1 Heat the oil and fry the onion and garlic until lightly browned.

2 Add the mushrooms, passata and seasoning. Simmer for 5 minutes.

3 Meanwhile cook the pasta according to the instructions on the packet.

4 Take the sauce off the heat, add the crabmeat and the cooked, drained pasta. Mix well, adjust the seasoning and serve.

Cook's tip

You can use canned tomatoes instead of the passata (5 Points per serving).

Variation

This also works well with tuna in brine – remember to adjust the Points.

2½ Points per serving

10 Total Points per recipe

125 Calories per serving

4 Servings

Freezing recommended. Preparation and cooking time: 25 minutes.

Give ordinary burgers a bit of zing with this speedy spicy alternative. Turkey burgers make a change from beef or chicken burgers, and all you have to do is mix all the ingredients together and grill! Serve with salad or in burger rolls. Remember to add on the Points.

450 g (1 lb) minced turkey

1 onion, grated

2 garlic cloves, crushed

1 teaspoon paprika

salt

1 Preheat the grill to medium.

2 Mix all the ingredients together.

3 Shape the mixture into 8 burgers.

4 Grill under medium heat for 4–5 minutes each side until the meat is cooked.

Weight Watchers tip

Turkey is so low in fat, you can afford to make this a regular item on the menu.

Pork Chops with Cheese

4½ Points per serving

9½ Total Points per recipe

210 Calories per serving

2 Servings

Freezing not recommended. Preparation and cooking time: 15 minutes + 1 hour marinating.

Mustard and cheese give this dish a mouthwatering taste.

1 garlic clove, crushed
½ teaspoon black peppercorns, coarsely ground
½ teaspoon dried rosemary
juice of 1 lemon
2 medium loin pork chops, fat removed
25 g (1 oz) half-fat Cheddar cheese, grated
½ teaspoon English mustard
salt

1 Mix together the garlic, salt, pepper, rosemary and lemon juice. Rub this mixture over both sides of the chops. Leave covered in the fridge for 1 hour.
2 Heat a griddle pan to very hot and grill each chop for 7 minutes on each side.
3 Mix the cheese with the mustard. Spread this over the chops. Grill the chops until the cheese is golden brown.

Minted Turkey Mince

3 Points per serving

11½ Total Points per recipe

145 Calories per serving

4 Servings

Freezing not recommended. Preparation and cooking time: 25 minutes.
This versatile dish can be used as a filling for pitta breads or jacket potatoes or it can be served with rice. Remember to add on the extra Points.

500 g (1 lb 2 oz) turkey mince
2 small onions, sliced thinly
2 tablespoons mint sauce
4 tablespoons low-fat plain yogurt
salt and freshly ground black pepper

1 In a non-stick pan, fry the turkey mince until it becomes lightly coloured.
2 Add the onions and stir the mixture until lightly browned.
3 Stir in the remaining ingredients and bring to the boil.
4 Cover and simmer on a low heat until the meat is cooked.

Variation
Minced chicken can be used instead. Remember to alter the Points. The Calories will remain the same.

Egg and Potato Nests

3 Points per serving

12½ Total Points per recipe

200 Calories per serving

4 Servings

Freezing not recommended. Preparation time: 25 minutes + 15 minutes baking.
These nests are a meal in themselves, just needing a salad as an accompaniment. They will also look impressive as part of a dinner party menu.

450 g (1 lb) potatoes, peeled and cut into quarters
15 g (½ oz) low-fat spread
3 tablespoons semi-skimmed milk
1 tomato, sliced
25 g (1 oz) half-fat Cheddar cheese, grated
4 small eggs
salt and freshly ground black pepper

1 Preheat the oven to Gas Mark 4/180°C/ 350°F
2 Cook the potatoes in boiling water until they are tender.
3 Mash them well with the low-fat spread and the milk.
4 Spoon the mash into nest shapes on a greased baking tray. Make sure the nests are deep enough to hold an egg.
5 Put a tomato slice in the bottom of each nest and sprinkle on some cheese.
6 Break an egg into each nest, sprinkle with the remaining cheese and season.
7 Bake for 15 minutes or until the eggs have set.

Pork Chops with Cheese
Mushrooms au Gratin **Page 39**

Tangy Welsh Rarebit

2 Points per serving

8½ Total Points per recipe

145 Calories per serving

4 Servings

Freezing not recommended. Preparation and cooking time: 15 minutes.
A family favourite with a difference!

75 g (3 oz) grated half-fat Cheddar cheese
a dash of Worcestershire sauce
2 tablespoons semi-skimmed milk
4 medium slices bread
3 tomatoes, sliced

1 Preheat the grill.
2 Mix the cheese, Worcestershire sauce and milk in a bowl.
3 Toast one side of the bread only.
4 Spread the cheese mixture over the untoasted side of the bread and place the sliced tomatoes on top.
5 Put the toast back under the grill until the cheese starts to bubble and turns light brown.

Weight Watchers tip
Use wholemeal bread instead of white to increase your fibre intake.

 ## Spicy Baked Beans

1 Point per serving

4 Total Points per recipe

80 Calories per serving

4 Servings

Freezing not recommended. Preparation and cooking time: 10 minutes.
This quick bean dish is full of Indian flavour. Serve immediately on wholemeal toast. Remember to add the Points.

1 teaspoon vegetable oil
1 teaspoon cumin seeds
1 onion, chopped
420 g Weight Watchers from Heinz reduced-sugar baked beans
½ teaspoon paprika or ½ teaspoon red chilli powder (if you like it hotter!)
1 teaspoon ground cumin

1 Heat the oil in a non-stick pan and add the cumin seeds and onion. Cook until the onions are lightly browned.
2 Add the baked beans and then the paprika or chilli powder and cumin.
3 Cook gently over a low heat until the beans are warmed through.

Weight Watchers tip
Baked beans are an excellent source of fibre.

Low Point Sandwich

4 Points per serving

15½ Total Points per recipe

215 Calories per serving

4 Servings

Freezing not recommended. Preparation time: 10 minutes.
Add as much tomato, cucumber and lettuce as you want to this sandwich – you won't be increasing the Points.

175 g (6 oz) diet cottage cheese
227 g can mixed fruit cocktail in water, drained
8 medium slices granary bread
freshly ground black pepper

1 Mix the cottage cheese and the fruit together.
2 Spread generously on each slice, season and serve.

Variation
Any type of bread can be used. Remember to adjust the Points.

Chicken and Vegetable Kebabs

2 Points per serving

8 Total Points per recipe

130 Calories per serving

4 Servings

Freezing not recommended. Preparation and cooking time: 30 minutes + 15 minutes marinating.
Kebabs are equally good whether cooked under a grill or on a barbecue.

250 g (9 oz) skinless, boneless chicken breasts, cut into 2 cm (¾-inch) cubes
2 tablespoons light soy sauce
2 cm (¾-inch) piece of fresh root ginger, sliced into thin strips
1 garlic clove, crushed
125 g (4½ oz) button mushrooms
1 red pepper, de-seeded and cut into squares
4 small onions, quartered
1 tablespoon vegetable oil

1 Place the chicken in a shallow dish and mix in the soy sauce, ginger and garlic. Cover and leave in the fridge for 15 minutes. Preheat the grill to high.

2 Drain the chicken, reserving the marinade. Thread a cube of chicken on to a small bamboo skewer, follow this with a mushroom, then a piece of pepper and then an onion quarter. Continue until everything is used up. Lightly brush with oil.

3 Grill for 4 minutes on each side until the kebabs are cooked; baste frequently with the marinade. Serve immediately.

Cook's tip
Soak bamboo skewers for 5 minutes before use to prevent burning.

Chicken and Vegetable Kebabs

 **Banana Delight**

(V)

3½ Points per serving

200 Calories per serving

1 Serving

Freezing not recommended. Preparation time: 2 minutes maximum!
Fast and tasty – an ideal combination that is both filling and low in Points.

1 crusty wholemeal roll
½ small banana (50 g/1¾ oz in weight)
40 g (1½ oz) plain cottage cheese

1 Slice open the wholemeal roll. Mash the banana and spread on the roll.
2 Spread the cottage cheese over the top and eat!

Variations

Chop ½ apple into the cottage cheese instead of using banana (deduct ½ Point per serving or 15 Calories), or try some canned mandarin oranges in natural juice.

 **Rice Tower**

(V)

1½ Points per serving

110 Calories per serving

1 Serving

Freezing not recommended. Preparation time: 5 minutes.
A fast and crunchy alternative to sandwiches – and it's healthy too! If you've tried rice cakes, here's your chance to experiment. This dish is so low in Points that you can afford to have a double portion. Just have a glance at those tempting variations.

25 g (1 oz) low-fat soft cheese
2 rice cakes
Marmite
½ medium apple, sliced
2 celery sticks

1 Spread the half-fat soft cheese on to the rice cakes.
2 Spread Marmite thinly over the top.
3 Top with crunchy apple slices and serve with celery sticks.

Cook's tip

Serve immediately to prevent the rice cakes from becoming soft.

Weight Watchers tip

Marmite is an excellent low-Calorie source of B vitamins and goes well with cheese and apple. Make sure you buy low-fat soft cheese rather than full-fat or reduced-fat – it is much lower in Calories.

 **Cheesy Pears**

(V)

1½ Points per serving

6 Total Points per recipe

80 Calories per serving

4 Servings

Freezing not recommended. Preparation time: 5 minutes.
This recipe is so simple, but has been a family favourite for many years, served with shredded lettuce and tomato slices. The sweetness of the pears blends well with the sharpness of the low-fat dressing.

410 g canned pear halves in natural juice, drained
4 dessertspoons Weight Watchers from Heinz low-fat salad dressing
60 g (2 oz) half-fat Cheddar cheese, grated

1 Place the pears on a serving plate.
2 Spoon 1 dessertspoon of low-fat dressing over each pear.
3 Top with the cheese.

Cook's tip

You need 4 pear halves for this recipe. I find a large can usually has this amount.

Weight Watchers tip

This is delicious served with a medium slice of crusty wholemeal bread (add 1 Point or 75 Calories).

Curried Chicken Flan

2 Points per serving

11 Total Points per recipe

110 Calories per serving

6 Servings

Freezing not recommended. Preparation time: 15 minutes + 45 minutes cooking. Filo pastry gives this flan a lovely crunchy bite and helps keep the Points down. You can buy the filo pastry in sheets from the chiller cabinet. Don't be afraid to try it if you've never used it before. The step-by-step method will help give you confidence if you're a beginner. Serve cold with a rice salad or warm with roasted broccoli (remember to add the extra Points).

50 g (1¾ oz) filo pastry (about 5 sheets)
200 ml (7 fl oz) skimmed milk
2 eggs
1 teaspoon curry powder
1 small apple, chopped finely
1 small onion, chopped finely
175 g (6 oz) cooked chicken, shredded
salt and freshly ground black pepper

1 Preheat the oven to Gas Mark 5/190°C/ 375°F.

2 Using a 23 cm (9-inch) non-stick flan tin, lay the filo pastry sheets overlapping at different angles to form a pastry case. Brush each sheet with a little water to remove excess flour and make them stick together.

3 Trim the edges which are hanging over the edges of the flan tin. You can use the trimmings for the pastry case too – no one will see this once the filling is added. Simply place them on top of the filo pastry sheets.

4 Bake the pastry case blind for 15 minutes (see Cook's tip).

5 Meanwhile mix the milk, eggs, curry powder and salt and pepper in a jug.

6 Remove the pastry case from the oven and put the apple, onion and cooked chicken in the pastry case.

7 Pour the egg mixture over the filling ingredients.

8 Bake for a further 30 minutes.

Cook's tip

'Baking blind' means baking the pastry case without its filling. Line the flan tin with pastry and prick the base of the pastry all over with a fork. Line it with a piece of greaseproof paper and fill with dried beans or uncooked rice which you should keep specially for this purpose. Remove the paper and rice or beans after baking blind and before adding your filling!

Curried Chicken Flan

Croissants Monsieur

6½ Points per serving

25 Total Points per recipe

285 Calories per serving

4 Servings

Freezing not recommended. Preparation time: 10 minutes + 10–15 minutes cooking.

A new look to an old French favourite. You will find the dough in the chiller cabinet at the supermarket under the brand name 'Kool'. Serve with salad garnish.

1 can of chilled croissant dough

6 slices wafer-thin ham

50 g (1¾ oz) half-fat Cheddar cheese, grated

1 Preheat the oven to Gas Mark 6/200°C/400°F.

2 Unroll the croissant dough and divide into 6 triangles (you will find it is pre-cut and so divides easily).

3 Place a slice of wafer-thin ham on each.

4 Roll up the croissants and place on a lined baking sheet.

5 Sprinkle with grated cheese.

6 Bake for 10–15 minutes until golden brown.

Croissants Monsieur

Prawn Cocktail Salad

1½ Points per serving

5½ Total Points per recipe

80 Calories per serving

4 Servings

Freezing not recommended. Preparation time: 10 minutes + 30 minutes chilling. Nothing beats prawn cocktail. Here is a recipe for marie rose sauce that is lower in Points and just as tasty as the original. Serve the cocktail with lemon wedges, tomato slices and salad leaves (a ready-washed, mixed packet is easiest). Decorate with a sprinkling of paprika over the top. Scrumptious!

200 g (7 oz) prawns, fresh or defrosted
*   thoroughly and drained*

For the sauce
4 tablespoons Weight Watchers from
*   Heinz low-fat salad dressing*
2 tablespoons tomato ketchup
2 tablespoons low-fat plain yogurt
1 teaspoon finely grated onion
salt and white pepper

1 Mix all the sauce ingredients together in a bowl and cover with cling film.

2 Chill in the fridge for at least ½ hour for the flavours to blend together.

3 Add the drained prawns, and mix in, making sure they are coated in sauce.

Cook's tip
Grate the onion on the finest part of your grater – it almost turns into a liquid that can then be added to the sauce.

 ## Mushrooms au Gratin

Ⓥ

1 Point per serving

3 Total Points per recipe

55 Calories per serving

4 Servings

Freezing not recommended. Preparation and cooking time: 15 minutes. Open mushrooms have a really good flavour.

4 large flat mushrooms
1 dessertspoon lemon juice
50 g (1¾ oz) half-fat grated Cheddar
*   cheese*
1 teaspoon Worcestershire sauce
salt and freshly ground black pepper
a little salad to garnish

1 Preheat the grill to medium. Remove the stalks from the mushrooms. Place the mushroom caps the right way up in a grill pan. Season and sprinkle them with a little lemon juice and grill for 2 minutes.

2 Turn them over and fill with the cheese. Sprinkle with Worcestershire sauce.

3 Grill until the cheese has melted and is beginning to brown.

4 Serve with the salad garnish.

Cook's tip
You might want to line the grill pan with foil in case the cheese oozes out.

Variation
If you are an olive lover try some chopped black olives on top of the cheese and a sprinkling of dried oregano. 2 stoned olives will add 0 Points, but 6 Calories.

 ## Turkey Baguettes

3½ Points per serving

14 Total Points per recipe

85 Calories per serving

4 Servings

Freezing not recommended. Preparation time: 10 minutes.
A great supper dish, ideal when you come in from those Christmas Sales and want something that's quick to prepare.

1 baguette
1 tablespoon low-fat spread
3 dessertspoons tomato relish
60 g (2 oz) wafer-thin turkey

1 Cut the baguette into quarters and cut open each piece.

2 Thinly spread the low-fat spread on one side and spread the tomato relish on the other.

3 Divide the turkey between the 4 sandwiches.

Weight Watchers tip
Leave out the low-fat spread and save ½ Point or 25 Calories per serving.

Variation
Smoked wafer-thin chicken or ham is good too.

Let's face it, we don't always eat lunch sitting at the table – we don't even eat from a plate – which is why this chapter is full of ideas for satisfying meals on the move. Take a Turkey and Raspberry Bagel to work, or try the Picnic Platter in the park. You won't need much excuse to indulge in these quick and easy feasts. They're great for the children's lunch boxes, for birthday parties and for a more sophisticated cocktail do at home. Tempt your guests with Stuffed Pitta with Tandoori Prawns or Smoked Turkey Rolls.

quick

lunches

Tuna Cocktail on Granary

7 Points per serving

14½ Total Points per recipe

385 Calories per serving

2 Servings

Freezing not recommended. Preparation time: 10 minutes.

A change from tuna and cucumber sarnies, this mix of beans and spring onions adds a truly Mediterranean feel.

200 g (7 oz) canned tuna in brine,
drained
420 g canned red kidney beans, drained
4 spring onions, sliced
fat-free vinaigrette dressing
4 medium slices granary bread
salt and freshly ground black pepper

1 Mix the tuna, beans and onions together and coat in the dressing. Season to taste.
2 Make sandwiches with the bread generously filled with this mixture.

Variations

Try sweetcorn instead of the kidney beans (Points per serving will be 6) and fresh chives in place of the spring onions. Green pepper works well too.

Weight Watchers tip

Choose tuna in brine in preference to tuna in vegetable oil.

Curried Egg Baps

(V)

7 Points per serving

270 Calories per serving

1 Serving

Freezing not recommended. Preparation and cooking time: 15 minutes.

Say 'curried egg' to most people and they'll think of a boiled egg in a curry sauce. This recipe uses scrambled spiced egg with crunchy spring onions stuffed into a warmed bap.

1 egg
½ teaspoon chilli powder
a pinch of salt
1 teaspoon oil
3 spring onions, sliced
1 large wholemeal bap, warmed
1 tablespoon low-fat plain yogurt

1 Beat the egg with the chilli powder and salt.
2 Heat the oil and fry the onions for a minute, then add the egg and stir frequently till cooked.
3 Fill the warmed bap with the egg mixture, top with the yogurt and serve hot or cold.

Turkey and Raspberry Bagels

4½ Points per serving

305 Calories per serving

1 Serving

Freezing not recommended. Preparation time: 5 minutes.

1 medium bagel, sliced open
4 slices wafer-thin honey-roast turkey
2 teaspoons low-calorie raspberry jam
shredded lettuce

1 Layer one side of the bagel with 2 slices of turkey, and then spread the jam on top.
2 Cover with another 2 slices of turkey and sprinkle the shredded lettuce on top. Top with the other bagel half and serve.

Stuffed Pitta with Tandoori Prawns

3 Points per serving

6 Total Points per recipe

200 Calories per serving

2 Servings

Freezing not recommended. Preparation and cooking time: 15 minutes. Tandoori dishes are favourites in Indian restaurants where the food is cooked quickly in a very hot clay oven. In this recipe prawns are cooked over a high heat in tandoori spices, which are available in the dried herbs section in supermarkets.

1 teaspoon tandoori spice mix

2 tablespoons low-fat plain yogurt

1 teaspoon lemon juice

125 g (4½ oz) fresh prawns or defrosted frozen prawns

1 teaspoon corn oil

1 small onion, chopped finely

2 tablespoons chopped fresh coriander leaves

1 medium wholemeal pitta bread, warmed

a few lettuce leaves, shredded

fresh lemon wedges

1 Blend together the spice mix, yogurt, lemon juice and prawns.

2 Heat the oil in a non-stick frying pan. Fry the onion until brown.

3 Turn up the heat to high and add the prawn mixture. Cook quickly, stirring frequently for about 5 minutes until the liquid is absorbed but not too dry.

4 Stir in the coriander.

5 Slit the pitta bread open and stuff with the lettuce. Add the tandoori prawns and serve with lemon wedges.

Stuffed Pitta with Tandoori Prawns

Cheese and Crunchy Apple Sandwich

Ⓥ

5½ Points per serving

330 Calories per serving

❶ Serving

Freezing not recommended. Preparation time: 10 minutes.

50 g (1¾ oz) half-fat Cheddar cheese, grated
½ red apple, grated
1 tablespoon unsweetened apple juice
2 medium slices soft-grain white bread
salt and freshly ground black pepper

1 Mix the cheese and apple together and add the apple juice. Season to taste.
2 Fill the sandwich generously with this mixture and serve immediately.

Cook's tip
This sandwich can't be prepared too far ahead, since the apple juice can make the bread soggy.

Variation
Try grated carrot and fat-free vinaigrette instead of the apple and apple juice. Reduce the Points by ½. The Calories remain the same.

Peanut Butter and Banana Sandwich

Ⓥ

7 Points per serving

395 Calories per serving

❶ Serving

Freezing not recommended. Preparation time: 5 minutes.

This is a sandwich that will never go out of fashion and it's healthy too. Peanut butter is high in fat so it's not a good idea to eat too much, but mix it with fruit and use it as a sandwich filling and you can have all the flavour and fun, but not at a great Calorie or Point cost.

1 small banana, peeled and mashed
2 heaped teaspoons crunchy peanut butter
1 tablespoon raisins
2 medium slices wholemeal bread

1 Mix the banana with the peanut butter and raisins and spread this evenly between the two slices of bread.

 ## 'Phili' and Grape Sarnie

Ⓥ

4½ Points per serving

275 Calories per serving

❶ Serving

Freezing not recommended. Preparation time: 10 minutes.

This sandwich has a truly tropical taste because it's scattered with fresh passion fruit seeds.

40 g (1½ oz) light Philadelphia soft cheese
2 medium slices bread
6 seedless grapes, halved
seeds of 1 passion fruit

1 Spread the cheese over one slice of bread.
2 Lay the grapes on top and scatter over the passion fruit seeds. Top with the other slice of bread.

Hummous Dip with Pitta Bread

(V)

4 Points per serving

17 Total Points per recipe

275 Calories per serving

4 Servings

Freezing: not recommended. Preparation time: 15 minutes.

175 g (6 oz) reduced-fat hummous
3 tomatoes, chopped
6 cm (2½-inch) piece of cucumber, diced
3 spring onions, sliced
1 tablespoon vinaigrette
4 medium pitta breads, warmed
salt and freshly ground black pepper

1 Mix together the hummous, tomatoes, cucumber, spring onions and vinaigrette. Season to taste.
2 Cut the warmed pitta bread into strips, and serve with the hummous dip.

Weight Watchers tip
Even reduced-fat hummous can make the Points mount up. Adding chopped vegetables helps it go further and adds texture.

New York Rolls

5 Points per serving

20 Total Points per recipe

235 Calories per serving

4 Servings

Freezing not recommended. Preparation time: 10 minutes.
If you've not been a big fan of oily fish up to now, have a go at this dish in which a fresh citrus sauce provides a contrasting flavour to some savoury herrings.

1 orange, segmented and chopped
6 tablespoons low-fat plain yogurt
200 g (7 oz) canned herring fillets in
*   savoury sauce, flaked*
4 sesame seed rolls, split open

1 Mix the orange segments with the yogurt.
2 Use the flaked herring to fill the roll. Spoon the yogurt and orange mixture on top, and serve.

Weight Watchers tip
Oily fish is high in Calories but it's an excellent source of omega-3 fatty acids.

'Bacon' and Banana Sandwich

3½ Points per serving

14½ Total Points per recipe

270 Calories per serving

4 Servings

Freezing not recommended. Preparation and cooking time: 15 minutes.

8 medium slices wholemeal bread
3 medium, ripe bananas, peeled and
*   mashed*
4 medium turkey rashers, grilled

1 Sandwich the bread slices together with the mashed banana and the warm turkey rashers.

Cook's tip
This sandwich is best eaten immediately.

Weight Watchers tip
Turkey rashers are a low-fat alternative to bacon.

 Melba Cream Tea

2 Points per serving

3½ Total Points per recipe

125 Calories per serving

2 Servings

Freezing not recommended. Preparation time: 10 minutes.

A variety of toppings on Melba toasts makes an unusual tea party for two.

8 slices Melba toast (available in packets)

2 teaspoons light Philadelphia soft cheese with garlic and herbs

1 teaspoon snipped chives or a sprinkling of dried chives

2 teaspoons plain fromage frais

1 heaped teaspoon low-calorie raspberry jam

2 slices wafer-thin honey-roast ham or turkey

1 slice reduced-fat Singles processed cheese, halved

8 thin slices cucumber, halved

a few leaves of lettuce

1 Spread 2 Melba toasts with the soft cheese and sprinkle the chives on top.

2 Spread another 2 Melba toasts first with the fromage frais and then with the jam.

3 Lay the ham or turkey over 2 more Melba toasts and top each with half a slice of processed cheese.

4 Lay the cucumber semi-circles decoratively over the remaining 2 Melba toasts.

5 Arrange the toasts on top of the lettuce leaves on a large (preferably oval) plate and serve.

 Lamb Sticks with Yogurt Dip

5½ Points per serving

22½ Total Points per recipe

215 Calories per serving

4 Servings

Freezing recommended. Preparation and cooking time: 30 minutes.

In this recipe, lean minced lamb is cooked on skewers. Lamb sticks can be served either with a side salad or in pitta bread. They're a bit like an up-market sausage and are equally good whether cooked under a grill or on a barbecue.

300 g (10½ oz) lean minced lamb

1 garlic clove, crushed

1 cm (½-inch) piece root ginger, crushed

½ teaspoon salt

2 teaspoons paprika

1 teaspoon cumin seeds

2 tablespoons chopped fresh mint

2 tablespoons chopped fresh parsley

2 tablespoons low-fat plain yogurt

170 g Healthy Eating yogurt and cucumber dip

1 Preheat the grill to medium. Mix together all the ingredients except the dip.

2 Take a level tablespoon of the mixture and shape it around one end of a skewer to form a sausage shape. Repeat with the rest of the mixture and the skewers.

3 Grill the sticks for 10–15 minutes until well browned, turning the sticks often. Serve with the dip.

Cook's tip

The sticks can be prepared a day ahead and stored uncooked and covered in the fridge.

Weight Watchers tip

If you want to reduce the Points even further, leave out the dip and serve with a green salad.

Variations

Try making these with skinless minced chicken or turkey. Remember to adjust the Points. Calories will be 155 per serving. Or try serving the sticks with Exotic Dip (page 14).

Chinese Take-away

(V)

1 Point per serving
3½ Total Points per recipe
150 Calories per serving
4 Servings

Freezing not recommended. Preparation time: 10 minutes.
A cold Chinese salad which is also great stir-fried with garlic.

410 g canned bean sprouts
425 g canned baby corn cobs, sliced
227 g canned water chestnuts, halved
½ green pepper, de-seeded and diced
½ red pepper, de-seeded and diced
½ teaspoon sesame seeds

For the dressing
1 tablespoon sesame oil
2 tablespoons soy sauce
2 teaspoons runny honey
a few drops of chilli sauce
coarse black pepper or dill pepper

1 Mix all the dressing ingredients together.
2 Pour this over the vegetables. Toss everything together, sprinkle with sesame seeds and serve.

Picnic Platter

(V)

4 Points per serving
15 Total Points per recipe
190 Calories per serving
4 Servings

Freezing not recommended. Preparation time: 15 minutes.

150 g (5½ oz) reduced-Calorie coleslaw
1 tablespoon raisins
a sprinkling of paprika powder
125 g (4½ oz) cottage cheese
100 g (3½ oz) canned mandarins,
*   drained, or 2 mandarins, peeled*
*   and segmented*
250 ml (9 fl oz) plain low-fat yogurt
3 slices pickled beetroot, diced
125 g (4½ oz) low-fat plain fromage frais
⅓ teaspoon mint sauce
8 cm (3¼-inch) stick cucumber, cut
*   into strips*
2 carrots, cut into matchsticks
2 celery sticks, cut into 8 cm (3¼-inch)
*   sticks*
4 slices Melba toast
4 crispbreads
freshly ground black pepper

1 Mix the coleslaw with the raisins. Garnish with the paprika.
2 Mix the cottage cheese with the mandarins.
3 Mix the yogurt with the beetroot.
4 Mix the fromage frais with the mint sauce and pepper.

5 Arrange these dips in a tray with the vegetable sticks, Melba toast and crispbreads.

Picnic Platter
Chinese Take-away

 ## Fruity Club Sandwich

Ⓥ

4 Points per serving

16½ Total Points per recipe

295 Calories per serving

4 Servings

Freezing not recommended. Preparation time: 15 minutes.
A tasty snack with a refreshing flavour. You will need some cocktail sticks.

12 medium slices freshly made toast
crisp lettuce leaves
227 g canned pineapple rings in juice, drained well
200 g (7 oz) diet cottage cheese
mild mustard (optional)

1 Cover the first slice of the toast with lettuce leaves and a pineapple ring.
2 Top with the second slice of toast. Spread this slice with the cottage cheese and a little mustard (if using).
3 Top with the third slice of toast. Cut into 2 triangles and use cocktail sticks to keep everything in place.
4 Repeat with the remaining ingredients to make 4 club sandwiches.

Variation
4 slices of lean ham can be substituted for the cottage cheese. Adjust the Points to 3½ per serving and the Calories to 290 per serving.

 ## Cheesy Egg Sandwich

Ⓥ

4 Points per serving

16½ Total Points per recipe

285 Calories per serving

4 Servings

Freezing not recommended. Preparation and cooking time: 15 minutes.

3 eggs, hard-boiled and chopped
225 g (8 oz) diet cottage cheese
3 tablespoons Weight Watchers from Heinz 90% fat-free mayonnaise
a bunch of cress
8 medium slices bread
3 tomatoes, sliced
salt and freshly ground black pepper

1 Mash the eggs with the cottage cheese and the mayonnaise. Season. Stir in the cress.
2 Make up 4 sandwiches with this mixture and the tomatoes.

 ## Pitta Pockets

Ⓥ

6 Points per serving

23½ Total Points per recipe

355 Calories per serving

4 Servings

Freezing not recommended. Preparation time: 15 minutes.
The filling can also be used as a side salad.

400 g (14 oz) canned mixed bean salad
150 g (5½ oz) half-fat Cheddar cheese, grated
4 tomatoes, quartered
4 medium pitta breads, split in half
lettuce, shredded
salt and freshly ground black pepper

1 Drain the beans and reserve 50 ml (2 fl oz) of the liquid.
2 Stir in the cheese, tomatoes and the liquid. Season to taste.
3 Open up the halved pitta breads and fill with the bean mixture and some lettuce.

Bulging Seafood Purse

3½ Points per serving

10½ Total Points per recipe

135 Calories per serving

3 Servings

Freezing not recommended. Preparation time: 10 minutes.

4 seafood sticks, diced

50 g (1¾ oz) cooked prawns

1 apple, diced

4 teaspoons Weight Watchers from Heinz low-fat mild mustard dressing

3 mini pittas

4 crisp lettuce leaves, shredded

salt and freshly ground black pepper

1 Mix the seafood sticks, prawns, apple and dressing together. Season to taste.

2 Fill the pittas with some of the lettuce and then with the seafood mixture.

 ## Crunchy Vegetable Baguette

Ⓥ

4½ Points per serving

9 Total Points per recipe

320 Calories per serving

2 Servings

Freezing not recommended. Preparation time: 10 minutes.

125 g (4¼ oz) reduced-Calorie coleslaw

2 × 8 cm (3¼-inch) pieces french bread, cut open

8 cm (3¼-inch) piece cucumber, cut into strips

1 carrot, cut into thin 6–8 cm (2½–3¼-inch) sticks

a good pinch of dried mint

2 teaspoons mango chutney

1 Spread the coleslaw over one side of the bread.

2 Add the cucumber and carrot.

3 Add the mint and mango chutney. Top with the other half of the bread and serve.

Crunchy Vegetable Baguette

Smoked Turkey Rolls

1½ Points per serving

100 Calories per serving

1 Serving

Freezing not recommended. Preparation time: 5 minutes.

Great for entertaining, or simply for treating yourself! You'll need some cocktail sticks.

4 slices wafer-thin smoked turkey
½ teaspoon mint sauce
1 teaspoon Philadelphia Light soft cheese

1 Spread the slices of turkey with the mint sauce.

2 Cover this with a thin layer of cheese. Roll the turkey up and secure with a cocktail stick.

Variation

Try ham or smoked salmon instead of the turkey.

 ### Tangy Baked Chicken

1½ Points per serving

6½ Total Points per recipe

100 Calories per serving

4 Servings

Freezing recommended. Preparation and cooking time: 40 minutes.

Lemon and garlic give this chicken dish a delicious flavour. Serve hot or cold.

4 medium skinless chicken drumsticks
1 teaspoon garlic salt
juice of 1 lemon
1 tablespoon vegetable oil
1 tablespoon dried rosemary

1 Preheat oven to Gas Mark 4/180°C/ 350°F.

2 Make cuts in the chicken and sprinkle with the garlic salt. Pour the lemon juice over.

3 Brush with the oil and sprinkle the rosemary over the meat.

4 Place the chicken in a shallow ovenproof dish and bake for 30–35 minutes or until the meat is cooked.

Cook's tip

The drumsticks can be marinated in the salt and lemon juice a few hours before and stored in the fridge.

Super Egg Sarnie Club Class

Ⓥ

5½ Points per serving

370 Calories per serving

1 Serving

Freezing not recommended. Preparation time: 25 minutes.

An ideal sandwich to take to the office or to savour on your own in front of the telly.

3 medium slices wholemeal bread
4 teaspoons very-low-fat spread
4 crisp lettuce leaves
2 spring onions, chopped finely
1 tablespoon Weight Watchers from Heinz blue cheese dressing
1 medium egg, hard-boiled and cooled under a running cold tap
1 tablespoon fat-free Thousand Island dressing

1 Spread 2 slices of bread with half the spread.

2 Top each with a crisp lettuce leaf.

3 Mix the spring onions with the blue cheese dressing and sandwich between the 2 slices of bread.

4 Spread the top slice of bread with 1 teaspoon spread, and spread the remainder on the third slice.

5 Mash the egg with the Thousand Island dressing, and make into a club sandwich with the remaining lettuce leaves and the third slice of bread.

Cook's tip

Wrap in cling film or foil if you're taking the sandwich to the office or on a picnic.

French Vegetable Tartlets

V

½ Point per serving

9 Total Points per recipe

70 Calories per serving

12 Servings

Freezing not recommended. Preparation time: 15 minutes + 10 minutes baking. These little tartlets are surprisingly rich and filling, and can be served hot or cold, so they make ideal party or picnic food. If you plan to serve them cold, delay filling them until just before serving, so that they stay deliciously crisp.

12 slices low-calorie bread from a 400 g loaf
low-fat cooking spray
390 g canned Tesco's Ratatouille Provençale
freshly ground black pepper

1 Preheat oven to Gas Mark 6/200°C/ 400°F.
2 Cut out circles of bread using a 7 cm (3-inch) pastry cutter, or tumbler.
3 Spray each hole of a 12-hole bun or muffin tin with a couple of squirts of low-fat cooking spray.
4 Line the holes with circles of bread. Give each circle another couple of squirts of low-fat cooking spray and bake for 8–10 minutes until crisp and browned.
5 Meanwhile, heat up the ratatouille, (if serving hot).
6 Fill the tartlets with the ratatouille and season with black pepper before serving.

Cook's tip
When served hot, the tartlets make an original and delicious accompaniment to lamb chops or roast lamb.

Weight Watchers tip
Low-calorie bread has more air bubbles than ordinary bread, which makes it much lighter. That's why it works particularly well in this recipe, because the tartlets crisp up beautifully.

Cheesy Ham 'n' Chutney Bagels

5 Points per serving
19½ Total Points per recipe
295 Calories per serving
4 Servings

Freezing not recommended. Preparation time: 10 minutes.

Perfect to take on a picnic, these can be assembled in less time than it'll take you to read the recipe!

4 medium, low-fat New York bagels
4 teaspoons low-fat soft cheese
100 g (3½ oz) lean honey-roast ham
4 tablespoons pickle (whatever you like best)

1 Split the bagels in half and spread each with 1 teaspoon of soft cheese.
2 Divide the ham between the bagels and add 1 tablespoon of pickle.

Variation

Substitute cooked chicken for the ham. Remember to alter the Points. Add 5 Calories per serving.

Cheesy Ham 'n' Chutney Bagels

Sausage and Potato Skewers

4 Points per serving

11½ Total Points per recipe

165 Calories per serving

4 Servings

Freezing not recommended. Preparation and cooking time: 20 minutes.

This makes an exciting change from bangers and mash! You will need some small wooden skewers, soaked for 5 minutes so they don't burn.

8 small new potatoes, scrubbed

8 button onions, peeled

8 Healthy Eating low-fat pork chipolata
    sausages, cut into 3 cm (1¼-inch)
    lengths

For the marinade

80 g (3 oz) Patak's tandoori paste

50 g (1¾ oz) low-fat natural yogurt

1 Simmer the potatoes and onions in salted water until almost tender. Drain.

2 Add the sausage pieces to the potatoes. Mix the tandoori paste with the yogurt and add to the sausages and potatoes. Mix well.

3 Preheat the grill to medium.

4 Thread the sausages, onions and potatoes on to small wooden skewers.

5 Grill for 5–7 minutes turning occasionally and basting with the marinade.

Weight Watchers tip

To make the Points even lower, use fewer chipolata pieces and thread other vegetables, such as tomatoes and bay leaves, on to the skewer as well.

Variations

Instead of chipolatas, try fresh tuna or marinated cubes of Quorn. Remember to adjust the Points.

Salads and vegetables look colourful and tempting on the plate and they help to fill you up. They also add balance to your meals, providing vital minerals and vitamins, such as beta carotene and vitamin C (which helps you resist and fight infection). So try to get into the habit of serving at least one portion of vegetables at each meal.

To get the maximum goodness onto your plate serve vegetables raw as salads, garnishes or in dips. Bought dips and dressings can often be high in Points, since they are based on oils but, in this chapter, you'll find ideas for dips and dressings based on low-fat ingredients. Or you could try some of the salads which are drenched in ready-made fat-free dressings.

side salads

and vegetables

Herby New Potatoes

(V)

1½ Points per serving

2½ Total Points per recipe

125 Calories per serving

2 Servings

Freezing not recommended. Preparation and cooking time: 15 minutes.

1 vegetable stock cube
250 g (9 oz) new potatoes, scrubbed
   and sliced
1 small onion, chopped finely
½ teaspoon dried mint
salt and freshly ground black pepper

1 Make up the vegetable stock to 150 ml (¼ pint) with boiling water. Put in a pan with the potatoes, onion, mint and seasoning.
2 Bring to the boil, cover and simmer till all the water is absorbed and the potatoes are cooked. Add more water if necessary during cooking.

Variation
This is delicious when mixed with leftover cabbage or boiled carrots.

Shredded Carrot Salad

(V)

½ Point per serving

2 Total Points per recipe

75 Calories per serving

4 Servings

Freezing not recommended. Preparation time: 10 minutes.

4 carrots, grated
1 teaspoon mint sauce
50 g (1¾ oz) raisins
1 teaspoon poppy seeds
fat-free vinaigrette dressing

1 Mix all the ingredients together and serve.

Tangy Bean Salad

(V)

3½ Points per serving

7 Total Points per recipe

185 Calories per serving

2 Servings

Freezing not recommended. Preparation time: 10 minutes.

420 g canned mixed beans, drained
5 cm (2-inch) piece of cucumber, diced
2 tablespoons snipped chives
2 tablespoons fat-free vinaigrette

1 Simply mix all the ingredients together and serve chilled.

Weight Watchers tips
Beans are a filling, protein-rich addition to any meal.
   Using a fat-free dressing helps keep the Points low.

Mexican Kidney Beans

Ⓥ

2½ Points per serving

8 Total Points per recipe

110 Calories per serving

❸ Servings

Freezing not recommended. Preparation time: 5 minutes.

420 g canned red kidney beans, drained

4 tablespoons salsa sauce (use a ready-made one)

½ teaspoon paprika

3 tablespoons Greek-style natural yogurt

1 Mix together the beans, salsa sauce and most of the paprika.

2 Serve on individual salad plates and top each with a spoonful of yogurt. Sprinkle a little extra paprika on top.

Weight Watchers tip

Greek-style yogurt is higher in fat than standard plain yogurt, but you may be able to find a light version in some supermarkets. Points will be 2 per serving if you use a 0% fat version of Greek-style yogurt.

Mexican Kidney Beans

Mushrooms in Creamy Sauce

2 Points per serving

8 Total Points per recipe

100 Calories per serving

4 Servings

Freezing not recommended. Preparation and cooking time: 10 minutes.

418 g canned creamed sweetcorn
210 g canned creamed mushrooms
1 teaspoon dried dill
½ teaspoon dill pepper

1 Heat the sweetcorn and mushrooms together, being careful not to let the mixture boil.
2 Flavour with the dill weed and pepper just before serving.

Minted Potato Salad

1½ Points per serving

5 Total Points per recipe

125 Calories per serving

3 Servings

Freezing not recommended. Preparation time: 5 minutes + chilling.

540 g can new potatoes, drained and halved
1 teaspoon dried mint
2 tablespoons Weight Watchers from Heinz low-fat mild mustard dressing
3 tablespoons snipped chives
salt and freshly ground black pepper

1 Mix the potatoes with the mint and toss in the dressing. Season to taste.
2 Put into a serving dish and decorate with the chives. Serve chilled.

Creamy Garlic Mash

2 Points per serving

8½ Total Points per recipe

140 Calories per serving

4 Servings

Freezing not recommended. Preparation and cooking time: 25 minutes.

450 g (1 lb) potatoes, chopped
½ teaspoon garlic salt or to taste
150 ml (¼ pint) skimmed milk
1 tablespoon Philadelphia Light soft cheese with garlic and herbs
4 teaspoons half-fat butter
a few sprigs of fresh parsley

1 Boil the potatoes with the garlic salt until tender.
2 Drain and mash the potatoes with the milk, cheese and butter. Serve hot, garnished with parsley sprigs.

Variation
You can use a fresh garlic clove if you prefer.

Southern Fries

 ## Barbecue Beans

V

2½ Points per serving

5 Total Points per recipe

155 Calories per serving

2 Servings

Freezing not recommended. Preparation time: 5 minutes + 15 minutes cooking. Chips will always be tempting, but traditional fried chips contain a lot of fat and many people find lower-fat oven chips less tasty. So here's a recipe that will give those oven chips a bit more zing!

200 g (7 oz) 5%-fat oven chips
1 teaspoon Cajun seasoning
½ teaspoon Schwartz chicken seasoning
¼ teaspoon herb pepper
a pinch of salt

1 Preheat the grill to medium. Line the grill pan with cooking foil.

2 Place the frozen chips in one layer in the pan and sprinkle them with all the seasonings.

3 Cook under the grill for 10–12 minutes until the chips are browned and cooked through. Serve at once.

Variation

You can use this spice mix for a combination of roasted vegetables too – it goes well with parsnips (par-boil them first).

V

1½ Points per serving

3 Total Points per recipe

135 Calories per serving

2 Servings

Freezing not recommended. Preparation and cooking time: 5 minutes.

420 g Weight Watchers from Heinz
*   Baked Beans*
2 tablespoons Worcestershire sauce
1 tablespoon soy sauce
a few drops of Tabasco sauce
freshly ground black pepper

1 Heat the beans with the sauces. Season with pepper and serve hot.

Southern Fries

Hawaiian Sweetcorn

Ⓥ

2 Points per serving

6½ Total Points per recipe

90 Calories per serving

❸ Servings

Freezing not recommended. Preparation and cooking time: 10 minutes.

Give a can of corn a lift with this sweet 'n' sour treatment, flavoured with pineapple and coconut.

326 g canned sweetcorn
3 tablespoons pineapple pieces in fruit
juice, drained
1 heaped tablespoon desiccated coconut

1 Heat the sweetcorn with the pineapple.
2 Serve on a flat dish and sprinkle the coconut on top.

Cook's tip

If you have time, toast the coconut under the grill for a few seconds before serving.

Brown Rice Salad

Ⓥ

3 Points per serving

11½ Total Points per recipe

160 Calories per serving

❹ Servings

Freezing not recommended. Preparation time: 5 minutes + 30 minutes cooking. This colourful rice salad not only tastes delicious but looks tantalising too.

125 g (4½ oz) brown rice
1 small red pepper, de-seeded and diced
200 g (7 oz) canned sweetcorn drained
3 tablespoons sultanas
2 tablespoons fat-free dressing
salt and freshly ground black pepper
4 spring onions, sliced, to garnish

1 Cook the rice in a large saucepan of lightly salted boiling water for about 30 minutes, or until it is tender. Drain thoroughly and cool.
2 Tip the rice into a bowl and add the pepper, sweetcorn and sultanas. Season to taste.
3 Toss lightly with the dressing. Garnish with the onions.

Weight Watchers tip

Wholegrains like brown rice are unrefined, so they have kept all their natural fibres, vitamins and minerals.

Mediterranean Tomato Salad

Ⓥ

1 Point per serving

4½ Total Points per recipe

105 Calories per serving

❹ Servings

Freezing not recommended. Preparation time: 15 minutes.

4 large firm, ripe tomatoes, sliced
into rings
1 large onion, sliced into rings
1 garlic clove, chopped finely
juice of 1 lemon
2 tablespoons olive oil
1 tablespoon white wine vinegar
2 tablespoons chopped fresh parsley
salt and freshly ground black pepper
(optional)

1 Arrange the tomatoes and the onion in a serving dish.
2 In a small bowl, mix together the garlic, lemon juice, olive oil and vinegar. Add some seasoning if you wish. Whisk until well mixed.
3 Pour the dressing over the salad and toss gently until the tomatoes and the onions are evenly coated. Garnish with the parsley.

Weight Watchers tip

Olive oil is a rich source of mono-unsaturated fats. This type of fat is thought to be beneficial for the heart.

Potato and Onion Salad

Ⓥ

2 Points per serving

8 Total Points per recipe

140 Calories per serving

❹ Servings

Freezing not recommended. Preparation time: 20 minutes.

A great starter or side dish for those in a hurry!

450 g (1 lb) cold cooked potatoes
3 spring onions, chopped finely
150 g (5½ oz) Weight Watchers from
*   Heinz Mayonnaise-style dressing*
1 tablespoon snipped chives
salt and freshly ground black pepper

1 Cut the potatoes into small cubes and put in a large bowl.
2 Add the spring onions and season.
3 Add the mayonnaise and stir gently until everything is well coated.
4 Sprinkle with the chives.

Variation
Add 3 chopped, cooked, skinless frankfurters. This will add 2½ Points per serving and 220 Calories per serving.

Sweetcorn Salad

Ⓥ

1½ Points per serving

5 Total Points per recipe

35 Calories per serving

❹ Servings

Freezing not recommended. Preparation time: 10 minutes.

This versatile salad can be served as a starter, side salad or as a filling for jacket potatoes or pitta bread.

340 g canned sweetcorn lite in brine,
*   drained*
2 celery sticks, chopped finely
2 tomatoes, chopped
2 spring onions, chopped
1 tablespoon Weight Watchers from
*   Heinz low-fat dressing*
salt and freshly ground black pepper

1 Mix all the ingredients together in a bowl, season to taste and enjoy the crunchy taste.

 ## Indian Salad

Ⓥ

½ Point per serving

1 Total Point per recipe

55 Calories per serving

❹ Servings

Freezing not recommended. Preparation time: 10 minutes.

This is a delightful combination of taste and colour. It can be served as a starter or a side dish, and can help to add flavours to an otherwise plain meal

1 green pepper, de-seeded and chopped
6 radishes, sliced
1 tablespoon raisins
½ cucumber, sliced
300 g (10½ oz) packet of bean sprouts,
*   washed*
juice of 2 lemons
1 teaspoon dried mint
salt to taste

1 Simply mix all the ingredients together and serve chilled.

Portuguese Salad

1 Point per serving

3 Total Points per recipe

95 Calories per serving

4 Servings

Freezing not recommended. Preparation time: 10 minutes.

This is a quick delicious salad with Mediterranean flavours. Enjoy this dish with fresh french bread. Remember to add the Points.

½ cucumber, cut into 5 cm (2-inch) sticks

4 tomatoes, quartered

1 green pepper, de-seeded and sliced

1 lettuce, shredded

1 onion, sliced

120 g canned sardines in brine

100 ml (3½ fl oz) Nando Portuguese dressing or any fat-free dressing

freshly ground black pepper

1 Place all the ingredients in a salad bowl, add the dressing and toss gently.

Weight Watchers tip

Sardines are a good source of calcium and vitamin D.

Juicy Citrus Salad

Ⓥ

½ Point per serving

2 Total Points per recipe

95 Calories per serving

4 Servings

Freezing not recommended. Preparation time: 10 minutes.

This crunchy, colourful salad can be served as a starter or as a refreshing side dish.

½ crisp iceberg lettuce, shredded

½ cucumber, diced

4 tomatoes, chopped

3 celery sticks, chopped

4 carrots, grated

1 eating apple, chopped

298 g canned mandarins in natural juice, drained

1 Mix all the ingredients in a large bowl.

Variation

Any fresh salad vegetables and citrus fruits can be used.

Vegetables in Parsley Sauce

Ⓥ

1 Point per serving

4½ Total Points per recipe

95 Calories per serving

4 Servings

Freezing not recommended. Preparation and cooking time: 15 minutes.

This vegetarian dish is a tasty and nutritious accompaniment to any meal.

25 g sachet of Colman's parsley sauce

300 ml (½ pint) skimmed milk

454 g frozen mixed vegetables

freshly ground black pepper

1 Make up the sauce according to the instructions on the packet, using the skimmed milk.

2 Cook the vegetables as instructed on the packet. Drain and place in a serving dish.

3 Pour the parsley sauce over the vegetables. Sprinkle with a pinch of pepper and serve immediately.

Weight Watchers tips

Vegetables whether fresh, frozen or canned are all good sources of minerals and vitamins.

Don't overcook your vegetables or you'll lose most of the vitamins in the cooking water.

Brown Rice Salad **Page 62**
Portuguese Salad

Chick-pea and Potato Salad

V

3 Points per serving

12 Total Points per recipe

165 Calories per serving

4 Servings

Freezing not recommended. Preparation and cooking time: 15 minutes.
This is a very filling, high-fibre, low-fat dish. It takes advantage of canned vegetables so you can save time for more important things! It can be served hot or cold.

1 tablespoon vegetable oil
300 g (10½ oz) canned new potatoes,
*   drained and cubed*
1 garlic clove, crushed
1 teaspoon mustard seeds
400 g (14 oz) canned chick-peas in
*   brine, drained and rinsed*
225 g (8 oz) canned chopped tomatoes
2 tablespoons chopped fresh coriander
*   or 1 tablespoon mixed herbs*
2 tablespoons lemon juice
salt and freshly ground black pepper

1 Heat the oil in a large frying pan. Add the potatoes, garlic and mustard seeds. Stir-fry until the potatoes are tender.
2 Combine the chick-peas, spiced potato, tomatoes, coriander and lemon juice in a large bowl. Season to taste. Toss gently.

Broccoli and Bean Salad

V

1 Point per serving

4 Total Points per recipe

125 Calories per serving

4 Servings

Freezing not recommended. Preparation and cooking time: 10 minutes.
A great starter or side dish for those in a hurry!

400 g (14 oz) fresh broccoli florets
400 g (14 oz) canned mixed beans in
*   vinaigrette, drained*
1 red onion, sliced finely
½ lettuce, shredded
salt and freshly ground black pepper

1 Cook the broccoli florets in boiling water for 2 minutes (they will still be crisp). Drain and refresh under running cold water.
2 In a bowl mix together the broccoli florets with the beans, onion and lettuce.
3 Toss gently and season to taste.

Weight Watchers Tip
Beans not only provide protein, but are an excellent source of fibre.

Chick-pea and Potato Salad
Broccoli and Bean Salad

 ## Cucumber Raita

(V)

1 Point per serving

4½ Total Points per recipe

65 Calories per serving

4 Servings

Freezing not recommended. Preparation time: 10 minutes + chilling.

This is a deliciously cooling accompaniment to any spicy dish. The cumin gives it an authentic Indian flavour. The raita can also be served as a dip with fresh vegetable crudités.

½ cucumber, peeled and grated
450 g (1 lb) low-fat plain yogurt
½ teaspoon cumin powder
a pinch of coarsely ground pepper

1 Drain off the liquid from the grated cucumber.

2 Mix this with the yogurt.

3 Add the cumin and some pepper.

4 Serve chilled (see tip).

Cook's tip

It is important not to prepare this dish too far in advance, since the juice from the cucumber can make the raita runny.

Variation

You can add some chopped coriander leaves, which gives you extra flavour, colour and vitamins, but no Points or Calories!

 ## Spicy Tomato Salad

(V)

0 Points per serving

0 Total Points per recipe

18 Calories per serving

4 Servings

Freezing not recommended. Preparation time: 5 minutes + 15 minutes chilling.

A salad with a bit of a kick to it. This is a great way to spice up tomatoes and you can use the dressing for a variety of salad ingredients. If you're serving up an Italian meal for guests, try adding some chopped half-fat mozzarella cheese (add 1½ Points/ 85 Calories per 25 g) to mimic those Italian flag colours – red, green and white.

4 tomatoes, sliced
½ green pepper, cut into 2.5 cm
*   (1-inch) strips*
juice of 1 lemon
¼ teaspoon chilli powder
salt and freshly ground black pepper

1 Mix the tomato slices and the green pepper in a shallow dish.

2 Mix the lemon juice and chilli powder together and pour over the tomato and pepper. Season to taste.

3 Chill for at least 15 minutes before serving.

Cook's tip

Chilling the salad helps to bring out and blend the flavours.

 ## Marinated Carrots

(V)

½ Point per serving

1 Total Point per recipe

70 Calories per serving

4 Servings

Freezing not recommended. Preparation time: 15 minutes + overnight chilling.

Marinated carrots are wonderful served with cold meat – especially cold turkey on Boxing Day; but don't save the recipe for only then or you will be missing a vegetable treat.

1 onion, chopped roughly
340 g packet washed and ready-to-cook
*   carrot batons*
½ × 295 g can Campbells Condensed
*   Half-Fat Tomato soup*
1 teaspoon mustard
1 green pepper, cut into 1 cm (½-inch)
*   strips*
freshly ground black pepper

1 Cook the onion and carrot batons with a little water on full power in a microwave for 3 minutes. Drain.

2 In a saucepan mix the soup, mustard, green pepper, black pepper and 100 ml (3½ fl oz) water and heat to boiling point.

3 Add to the carrot and onion mixture, and chill overnight in the fridge before serving.

French Beans with Almonds

Ⓥ

1 Point per serving

3 Total Points per recipe

45 Calories per serving

❹ Servings

Freezing not recommended. Preparation time: 20 minutes + 10 minutes cooking. A great way to use up leftover French beans, but it's also worthwhile cooking them specially for this recipe.

300 g (10½ oz) French beans, topped and tailed
low-fat cooking spray
1 onion, chopped finely
25 g (1 oz) flaked almonds
salt and freshly ground black pepper

1 Boil the French beans in water until crunchy (about 10 minutes) and drain.
2 When cool enough to handle, cut the beans into approximately 2.5 cm (1-inch) lengths.
3 Spray a heavy-based frying pan with low-fat cooking spray (2 sprays per person). Heat the pan.
4 Add the onion and cook until brown. If necessary add 1 teaspoon water to prevent it sticking.
5 Add the beans and almonds and heat, stirring to prevent them sticking. Season to taste.

Cook's tip

Any fresh green beans are suitable for this recipe e.g. Kenyan, fine beans. Many can be bought already topped and tailed. Frozen green beans are not suitable, as they are not crunchy enough.

Variations

Toasted pumpkin seeds or sesame seeds can be used instead of flaked almonds. Points remain the same.

 ## Roasted Broccoli

Ⓥ

0 Points per serving

0 Total Points per recipe

35 Calories per serving

❹ Servings

Freezing not recommended. Preparation time: 5 minutes + 30 minutes cooking. This is a very tasty vegetable dish. The sesame seeds add crunch and colour. You can give it a Chinese flavour by using a few drops of sesame oil instead of the spray oil.

low-fat cooking spray
450 g (1 lb) fresh broccoli florets
1 teaspoon sesame seeds

1 Heat the oven to Gas Mark 8/230°C/ 450°F.
2 Spray a non-stick roasting tin with 4 sprays of low-fat cooking spray.
3 Add the broccoli florets and roll them around the tin.
4 Sprinkle with sesame seeds.
5 Bake for 30 minutes. Serve hot.

Cook's tip

Frozen broccoli is not suitable for this recipe, but if you are in a hurry use a packet of fresh, ready-prepared broccoli florets. Don't worry if the broccoli browns in the oven – this brings out the flavour.

Tuna Salade Niçoise

3½ Points per serving

14 Total Points per recipe

260 Calories per serving

4 Servings

Freezing not recommended. Preparation and cooking time: 20 minutes + 10 minutes cooling.

Ideal as a light lunch or supper dish, this recipe conjures up thoughts of the Mediterranean on a perfect summer's day.

1 crisp lettuce
4 medium eggs, hard-boiled, cooled and
*   halved lengthways*
4 medium tomatoes, quartered
550 g canned new potatoes, drained
225 g (8 oz) fine green beans, fresh or
*   frozen, cooked, drained and cooled*
355 g canned skipjack tuna chunks in
*   brine, drained*
4 tablespoons fat-free vinaigrette
*   dressing*
salt and freshly ground black pepper

1 Line a serving bowl with the crisp lettuce leaves.

2 Arrange the eggs, vegetables and tuna attractively on top.

3 Season with salt and freshly ground black pepper.

4 Toss in the fat-free vinaigrette dressing just before serving.

Cook's tips

The eggs can be cooled very quickly by putting them in a colander under a running cold tap. Ditto the beans. Both eggs and beans can be cooked in advance, so that the dish can be assembled at the last minute. Leave the eggs in their shells, in cold water until you need them. This prevents the edges of the yolks turning black which, though it doesn't affect the flavour, doesn't look very attractive.

The traditional version of this dish includes anchovies and black olives, so if you like them add a few of each. Adjust the Points as necessary.

Variation

Use a medium skinless cooked chicken breast instead of the tuna. Points will be 3 per serving. Calories will be 275 per serving.

Salad Waldorf

V

2 Points per serving

4 Total Points per recipe

140 Calories per serving

2 Servings

Freezing not recommended. Preparation time: 15 minutes.

This is perfect to serve with cold chicken or turkey, and is also great with seafood. On its own, or with cheese, it is ideal for vegetarians.

1 Cox's apple, peeled, cored and diced
juice of ½ lemon
crisp lettuce leaves
2 celery sticks, trimmed and chopped
175 g (6 oz) seedless grapes
3 tablespoons Weight Watchers from
    Heinz 90% fat-free mayonnaise
2 walnut halves, crushed, to garnish
salt and freshly ground black pepper

1 Toss the diced apple in the lemon juice.

2 Line a serving bowl with the crisp lettuce.

3 Drain the apple of lemon juice and combine with the celery and grapes. Toss in the mayonnaise and season to taste.

4 Spoon on top of the lettuce and serve garnished with the crushed walnut halves.

Weight Watchers tip

Save more Calories/Points by leaving out the walnuts. This will make the salad 1½ Points per serving or 120 Calories per serving.

Potato and Onion Layer

V

3 Points per serving

11 Total Points per recipe

240 Calories per serving

4 Servings

Freezing not recommended. Preparation time: 10 minutes + 1½ hours cooking.

This is a quick and easy dish to prepare, that can be left in the oven to cook while you get on with the more important jobs (like reading or watching TV...!)

1 kg (2 lb 4 oz) potatoes, peeled and cut
    into slices 5 mm (¼ inch) thick
1 large onion, sliced
300 ml (½ pint) vegetable stock, made
    with a stock cube and hot water

1 Preheat the oven to Gas Mark 4/180°C/ 350°F.

2 Place half the potatoes in a non-stick, shallow, ovenproof dish. No oil is needed.

3 Add the onions, and then top with the rest of the potato.

4 Pour over the hot stock and cover with a lid or cooking foil.

5 Bake in the oven for 1 hour.

6 Remove the lid or foil and pour away most of the stock – use a slotted spoon to help you keep the potatoes in place.

7 Turn the oven up to Gas Mark 9/240°C/ 475°F and return the dish to the oven for ½ hour to finish cooking and brown the top.

Tangy Mustard, Carrot and Parsnip Mash

Ⓥ

1½ Points per serving

6 Total Points per recipe

135 Calories per serving

❹ Servings

Freezing recommended. Preparation time: 10 minutes + 15–20 minutes cooking. Try serving this at a dinner party and just wait for the compliments!

350 g (12 oz) potatoes, peeled and sliced
2 carrots, peeled and sliced
225 g (8 oz) parsnips, peeled and sliced
2 teaspoons made English mustard (or according to taste)
salt and freshly ground black pepper

1 Put all the vegetables together into a large pan of boiling, salted water and cook for 15 minutes or until tender.

2 Drain well and mash until smooth.

3 Mix in the mustard, beat well and season to taste before serving.

Cook's tip

This mash goes very well with roast meats and casseroles. If serving at a dinner party, garnish with sprigs of fresh parsley just before you bring it to the table.

Variations

The mash works equally well using just the carrots and parsnips – it's lower in Calories and Points, too!

For a family supper, grill 8 thick reduced-fat pork sausages and serve with the mash. Calories will increase to 315 per serving, and Points to 5½ per serving.

We all have our favourites when it comes to meat dishes. There are those of us who prefer a bit of spice in life who will make the Szechuan Chicken with Green Pepper into a regular item on the family menu. And then there are those who like the reliable things in life and who will often be indulging in Welshman's Cottage Pie and Hearty Chicken Casserole. Whatever your preference, you'll find masses of tempting recipes in this chapter. They're quick too, as practical for midweek suppers as they are for weekend entertaining.

Most of us will be glad to see sausages and bacon put in an appearance (Sausage Risotto, and Bacon Ratatouille) and because we've used low-fat sausages and lean bacon, these are still Points-friendly recipes. It's a good idea generally to get into the habit of choosing lean meats, or buy cheaper versions and trim the fat off before cooking. I often buy chicken with the skin on and find that it slides off quite easily during preparation.

Remember also to use as little oil as possible. Often you'll find that there's enough 'hidden fat' in the meat and you don't need to add any more during cooking. Many of these recipes use low-fat cooking spray which is free from Points.

Meat is very nutritious. It's rich in iron and vitamin B12 and high in protein. However, as always, balance is the key and it's a good idea to ensure that you incorporate a variety of vegetables into your meals. Serve the meat dishes from this chapter with some of the colourful and tasty vegetables in other chapters. You'll find that the Creamy Chicken with Mushrooms goes particularly well with Mediterranean Tomato Salad or French Beans With Almonds. Pork Chops with Apple goes down a treat with Creamy Garlic Mash. Or try Lamb Steaks With Mint spiced up with Indian Salad. The list goes on. No doubt you'll find your own favourite combinations.

meat

and poultry

Tangy Turkey with Cranberries

1 Point per serving

4½ Total Points per recipe

285 Calories per serving

4 Servings

Freezing recommended after step 2.
Preparation and cooking time: 20 minutes.
A great recipe for just after Christmas.
Serve with plain brown boiled rice.
4 tablespoons of cooked rice adds
3 Points or 80 Calories per serving.

300 ml (½ pint) chicken stock made
*   with a stock cube*
125 g (4½ oz) dried cranberries
450 g (1 lb) cooked turkey, cut into
*   bite-size pieces*
2 teaspoons cornflour
grated zest and juice of 1 lemon
salt and freshly ground black pepper

1 Bring the stock to a simmer, add the
cranberries and simmer for 10 minutes.
2 Add the turkey and re-heat thoroughly.
3 Blend the cornflour with a little cold
water and add to hot turkey and stock.
4 Add the zest and a squeeze of lemon
juice and season to taste before serving.

Cook's tip
Fresh cranberries may be used. In this
case, reduce the stock a little, but simmer
for the same length of time until the
cranberries burst.

Creamy Chicken with Mushrooms

V

2 Points per serving

9½ Total Points per recipe

185 Calories per serving

4 Servings

Freezing recommended. Preparation and
cooking time: 30 minutes.
Need to conjure up a gourmet meal in
minutes? Use some condensed soup to
make a creamy sauce, throw in some
mushrooms and green pepper, flavour
with mustard – and enjoy! This recipe
provides four generous portions. Serve
with boiled rice.

2 teaspoons olive oil
6 shallots, quartered
1 green pepper, diced
2 medium skinless chicken breasts
*   (total weight around 250 g/9 oz),*
*   cut into strips*
2 heaped teaspoons whole-grain
*   mustard*
250 g (9 oz) mushrooms, sliced
295 g canned 99% fat-free Campbell's
*   Condensed Chicken Soup*
150 ml (¼ pint) skimmed milk
salt and freshly ground black pepper

1 Heat the oil in a wok or non-stick
saucepan. Fry the shallots and pepper
in the oil for about a minute.
2 Add the chicken and mustard, and stir-
fry for about 5 minutes until the chicken
turns brown.
3 Add the mushrooms and stir-fry for a
few minutes more. Add a little hot water if
it begins to stick on the bottom.
4 Pour in the soup and add the skimmed
milk. Allow the sauce to heat through,
adding some hot water if you prefer a
thinner sauce. Season to taste.

Pork Chops with Apple **Page 78**
Creamy Chicken with Mushrooms

Mandarin-stuffed Chicken Breast

Ⓥ

3 Points per serving

12½ Total Points per recipe

180 Calories per serving

❹ Servings

Freezing recommended. Preparation time: 15 minutes + 35 minutes cooking. I discovered this recipe by chance, because these were the only ingredients I had lying around. I was amazed at how delicious such a low-Point main meal could be, and it looked incredibly appetising. Might try this one on Valentine's day again...

You will also need some cocktail sticks.

298 g can mandarin oranges in natural juice
4 skinless chicken breasts (weighing around 500 g/1 lb 2 oz in total)
4 teaspoons Schwartz chicken seasoning
low-fat cooking spray
1 teaspoon cornflour
1 tablespoon chopped fresh parsley
salt and freshly ground black pepper

1 Preheat the oven to Gas Mark 6/200°C/ 400°F. Line a baking tray with foil. Drain the mandarins, reserving the juice.

2 Beat the chicken breasts with a rolling pin to flatten them.

3 Season each side with ½ teaspoon of chicken seasoning. Place each breast on a small square of cooking foil.

4 Set aside a few mandarins for decoration. Divide the remainder into 4 portions. Put the mandarins on one half of each chicken breast and fold the other half of the breast over the top, making a turnover shape. Secure each breast with one or two cocktail sticks.

5 Give each breast a couple of sprays of oil on each side and fold the foil over them. Place the chicken on the tray and cook in the oven for 25 minutes.

6 Meanwhile, make a paste with the cornflour and a few teaspoons of cold water. Put the mandarin juice in a measuring jug and add enough water to make it up to 150 ml (¼ pint). Heat the juice in a pan with the paste, stirring all the time until the sauce boils and thickens. Add a little more water if you prefer a thinner sauce and season to taste.

7 Take the chicken out of the oven and open up the foil so the chicken can brown. Return to the oven for a further 5–10 minutes.

8 Serve hot, topped with the mandarin sauce, a few mandarin slices and the chopped parsley.

Variation

Canned peaches or pineapple can be used instead of mandarins. Add 40 Calories per serving for pineapple; Calories stay the same for peaches.

Pork Chops with Apple

5 Points per serving

19½ Total Points per recipe

235 Calories per serving

❹ Servings

Freezing not recommended. Preparation time: 15 minutes + 1–1½ hours cooking. This appetising dish needs very little preparation. It can be left to cook in the oven while you get on with something else.

450 g (1 lb) onions, peeled
1 medium cooking apple, sliced
1 tablespoon sugar
4 × 100 g (3½ oz) pork loin chops, trimmed of fat
150 ml (¼ pint) unsweetened apple juice
2 whole cloves
freshly ground black pepper

1 Preheat the oven to Gas Mark 4/180°C/ 350°F.

2 Put the onions in a greased casserole dish (one with a lid). Sprinkle with pepper.

3 Cover with half the apple and sprinkle with the sugar.

4 Put the pork chops on top. Cover with the rest of the sliced apple.

5 Pour the apple juice over and add the cloves.

6 Put the lid on the casserole and bake for 1–1½ hours or until the pork is cooked.

Chicken Tikka Masala

V

8 Points per serving
16½ Total Points per recipe
400 Calories per serving
2 Servings

Freezing not recommended. Preparation and cooking time: 30 minutes + 20 minutes marinating.

It's not one of Britain's most popular meals for nothing. With this recipe, you won't believe it came out of a jar. Please do try this if you're a tikka masala lover – it's as good as any restaurant and much better than a supermarket ready meal.

450 g (1 lb) chicken breast, skinned and cubed
1 teaspoon oil
½ teaspoon cumin seeds
290 g jar Weight Watchers from Heinz Indian Tikka Masala Cooking Sauce
3 × 15 g (½ oz) packets fresh coriander leaves, chopped roughly

For the marinade
1 green chilli, chopped finely
1 teaspoon crushed garlic
1 teaspoon crushed ginger
250 ml (9 fl oz) low-fat plain yogurt

1 Make up the marinade and marinate the chicken in the mixture for at least 20 minutes.
2 Heat the oil over a medium heat and fry the cumin seeds for a few seconds.
3 Remove the chicken from the marinade and add to the pan. Cook over a high heat until the chicken changes colour (about 10 minutes).

4 Add the rest of the marinade and the cooking sauce. Bring to the boil, stirring constantly, and then cover and simmer for 20 minutes. Stir in the coriander just before serving.

Cook's tips
The yogurt may curdle – this won't affect the flavour, but if you don't like it you could add ½ teaspoon of cornflour to the marinade before heating it and stir vigorously as the sauce comes to the boil.

The coriander adds crunch as well as flavour and colour. The cheapest place to find it is in Asian grocery stores where you can often get a huge bunch more cheaply than a supermarket 15 g (½ oz) packet.

Chicken Tikka Masala

Beef with Crème Fraîche

4 Points per serving

15 Total Points per recipe

135 Calories per serving

4 Servings

Freezing not recommended. Preparation time: 15 minutes.

This dish makes a change from cold beef sandwiches! It can be served with a green salad or with crusty french bread. Remember to add on the extra Points.

200 g (7 oz) cold roast beef, cut
into strips

For the sauce

6 tablespoons Healthy Eating low-fat
crème fraîche

2 tablespoons low-fat plain yogurt

1 tablespoon horseradish sauce

a dash of Tabasco or other hot pepper
sauce

salt and freshly ground black pepper

1 Mix together the sauce ingredients.

2 Arrange the beef strips on a serving plate and spoon the sauce over the top.

Weight Watchers tip

To cut the Points down even further, increase the quantity of low-fat plain yogurt to 5 tablespoons and decrease the amount of crème fraîche to 3 tablespoons. Points per serving will be 3. Calories per serving will be 120.

Szechuan Chicken with Green Pepper

4 Points per serving

16½ Total Points per recipe

280 Calories per serving

4 Servings

Freezing not recommended. Preparation and cooking time: 30 minutes + marinating.

A Chinese take-away at home, this tasty treat is rich in flavour and is best served with plain boiled rice.

3 skinless chicken breasts (weighing
around 175 g/6 oz each), cut
into strips

2 teaspoons sesame oil

1 onion, sliced lengthways

1 green pepper, diced

1 teaspoon crushed garlic

175 g (6 oz) canned baby sweetcorn,
drained and sliced

225 g can water chestnuts, drained

Beef with Crème Fraîche

250 g (9 oz) frozen Chinese stir-fry
    vegetables
295 g jar Weight Watchers from Heinz
    Szechuan Cooking Sauce

For the marinade

2 teaspoons cornflour
2 tablespoons light soy sauce
freshly ground black pepper

1 Mix together the cornflour, soy sauce and pepper to make the marinade. Marinate the chicken in the mixture for anything between 5 minutes to 1 hour.
2 Heat the sesame oil in a large wok or non-stick frying pan. Fry the onion, pepper and garlic for 3–5 minutes.
3 Add the chicken pieces and stir-fry for about 10 minutes. Add some water if the mixture begins to stick on the bottom.
4 Stir in all the vegetables and stir-fry for a few minutes.
5 Add the sauce. Cover and cook until the chicken is tender and the vegetables are cooked but still crunchy.

Variation

Try adding 125 g (4½ oz) pineapple pieces for a sweet and sour touch. This will add 15 Calories per serving.

 ## Grilled Pork Chops

4 Points per serving
16 Total Points per recipe
170 Calories per serving
④ Servings

Freezing recommended. Preparation and cooking time: 20 minutes.
This tasty dish can be served with Creamy Garlic Mash (page 60) or Roasted Broccoli (page 69). Remember to add on the Points.

4 medium loin pork chops, trimmed
    of fat
1 teaspoon dried oregano
1 teaspoon dried marjoram
juice of 1 lemon
low-fat cooking spray
salt and freshly ground black pepper

1 Preheat the grill to medium.
2 Sprinkle both sides of the chops with the oregano, marjoram, lemon juice and salt and pepper. Spray with low-fat cooking spray (use about 2 sprays for each side of your chops).
3 Grill for 7–8 minutes on each side or until the meat is cooked.

 ## Chicken and Broccoli Bake

1½ Points per serving
6½ Total Points per recipe
105 Calories per serving
④ Servings

Freezing not recommended. Preparation and cooking time: 30 minutes.
This recipe is ideal for using up leftover meat. Any cooked meat can be used instead of the chicken, but white meat will help keep Points low.

100 g (3½ oz) frozen broccoli florets
25 g sachet Colman's Mushroom sauce
200 g (7 oz) cooked chicken, cut into
    small pieces.

1 Preheat the oven to Gas Mark 5/190°C/ 375°F.
2 Cook the broccoli florets in boiling water for 2 minutes and drain well.
3 Make up the sauce as instructed on the packet.
4 Place the cooked meat and the broccoli in an ovenproof dish.
5 Pour over the sauce and bake for 15 minutes.

Pork and Lamb Casserole

 **Shepherd's Pie**

 **Chicken Korma**

3 Points per serving

11½ Total Points per recipe

290 Calories per serving

4 Servings

6 Points per serving

24 Total Points per recipe

370 Calories per serving

4 Servings

4½ Points per serving

17½ Total Points per recipe

240 Calories per serving

4 Servings

Freezing recommended. Preparation and cooking time: 45 minutes.

This one-pot meal is ideal for cold winter evenings. You can vary the vegetables depending on what's available.

Freezing recommended. Preparation and cooking time: 45 minutes.

This family favourite can be prepared in advance and stored in the fridge until you're ready to pop it in the oven.

Freezing not recommended. Preparation and cooking time: 1 hour.

This curry has a thick flavoursome sauce and red and green peppers for extra colour. Serve with pitta bread or plain boiled rice (remember to add on the Points). It goes well with the Cucumber Raita (page 68) and the Indian Salad (page 63).

200 g (7 oz) pork tenderloin or fillet, cut into thin strips

100 g (3½ oz) lean leg of lamb, cut into thin strips

1 small cabbage, cut into thin wedges

4 carrots, chopped

2 onions, sliced

450 g (1 lb) new potatoes

450 ml (16 fl oz) vegetable stock

salt and freshly ground black pepper

450 g (1 lb) potatoes

3 tablespoons semi-skimmed milk

15 g (½ oz) light margarine

1 tablespoon vegetable oil

1 onion, chopped finely

1 garlic clove, crushed

450 g (1 lb) lean minced beef

150 ml (¼ pint) strong beef stock

15 g (½ oz) half-fat Cheddar cheese, grated

350 g (12 oz) boneless skinless chicken, cubed

1 red pepper, cut into chunks

1 green pepper, cut into chunks

440 g jar Tesco reduced-fat Korma sauce

fresh coriander leaves, to garnish

1 Put all the meat and the vegetables into a flameproof casserole.

2 Add the stock and seasoning.

3 Bring to the boil and then cover and simmer for 25–30 minutes, stirring occasionally, until the meat is cooked.

1 Preheat the oven to Gas Mark 6/200°C/400°F.

2 Cook the potatoes in boiling water. When they are tender, drain and mash them with the semi-skimmed milk and light margarine.

3 Heat the oil in a large frying pan and fry the onion for 3–4 minutes.

4 Add the garlic and the mince and cook, stirring, for 5 minutes.

5 Add the stock and bring to the boil, stirring continuously.

6 Transfer the mince to an ovenproof dish, top with the mashed potato and sprinkle with the cheese. Bake for 25 minutes.

1 Preheat the oven to Gas Mark 4/180°C/350°F.

2 Place the chicken and the peppers in an ovenproof dish and add the contents of the jar. Cover and cook for 50 minutes. Garnish with the coriander leaves.

Weight Watchers tip

Reduce the Points even further by leaving out the lamb and using more vegetables. Points will be reduced by ½ per serving. Calories will be 245 per serving.

Cook's tip

The sauce is available in mild, medium and hot varieties. The choice is yours!

Variation

Healthy Eating cubed pork can be substituted for the chicken. Points remain the same.

Bacon Chops with Cumberland Sauce **Page 92**
Pork and Lamb Casserole

Pork with Vegetables

4 Points per serving

16 Total Points per recipe

285 Calories per serving

4 Servings

Freezing not recommended. Preparation and cooking time: 30 minutes.

There are so many ready-made marinades available now that there is no need for bland food. These pork fillets are delicious with a tomato-based sauce.

450 g (1 lb) pork tenderloins or fillets, sliced into strips
1 bottle Lea & Perrins Sun-Dried Tomato and Herb Marinade
1 tablespoon vegetable oil
1 red pepper, sliced
6 tomatoes, quartered
150 g (5½ oz) frozen green beans

1 Marinate the pork for 5 minutes in half the Lea & Perrins marinade.

2 Heat the vegetable oil in a pan and fry the pork for 7–10 minutes over a low heat until cooked through.

3 Add the vegetables and continue to fry for a few minutes.

4 Add the remaining marinade to the pan and mix thoroughly. Let the mixture simmer over a low heat, until the vegetables are cooked but still a little crunchy.

Weight Watchers tip

Serve with jacket potatoes or pasta twists. Remember to add the Points.

 ## Pork in Mushroom Sauce

3½ Points per serving

13½ Total Points per recipe

210 Calories per serving

4 Servings

Freezing not recommended. Preparation and cooking time: 30 minutes.

450 g (1 lb) pork fillet or tenderloin cut into 8 slices
1 teaspoon vegetable oil
295 g canned 99% fat-free Campbell's Condensed Mushroom Soup
125 ml (4 fl oz) dry white wine
salt and freshly ground black pepper

1 Preheat the grill to medium.

2 Brush each side of the pork slices with the oil and grill for 8 minutes on each side or until the meat is cooked.

3 Put the pork in a flameproof dish. Add the soup and the wine. Heat gently, stirring, but don't allow the mixture to boil.

4 Season to taste.

Variation

You can make this with skinless chicken breast. Remember to adjust the Points. Calories per serving will be 190.

 ## Baked Bacon with Apricots

3½ Points per serving

14 Total Points per recipe

200 Calories per serving

4 Servings

Freezing not recommended. Preparation time: 5 minutes + 1 hour 10 minutes cooking.

This is a simple but delicious dish for a special meal or family dinner.

500 g (1 lb 2 oz) smoked bacon joint
410 g canned apricots in natural juice
chopped parsley

1 Preheat the oven to Gas Mark 5/190°C/375°F.

2 Place the bacon joint in a casserole.

3 Pour the apricots and juice over the joint and cover with a lid or some cooking foil.

4 Bake in the oven for 50 minutes, spooning the fruit over the meat occasionally.

5 Uncover and bake for a further 20 minutes.

6 To serve, slice the meat into 8 (2 slices each). Spoon over the apricots and juices and sprinkle with chopped parsley.

Variations

Use canned peaches in natural juice instead of the apricots, and try bacon chops, trimmed of fat, instead of the bacon joint.

Macaroni Pork

5 Points per serving
19 Total Points per recipe
385 Calories per serving
4 Servings

Freezing not recommended. Preparation and cooking time: 40 minutes.
This substantial dish is easy to prepare and you can add any variety of vegetables you like.

200 g (7 oz) short-cut macaroni
Colman's Cheese Sauce Mix
2 tablespoons vegetable oil
200 g (7 oz) Healthy Eating boneless
*   pork steak, cut into strips*
100 g (3½ oz) courgettes, sliced
200 g (7 oz) broccoli florets
25 g (1 oz) half-fat cheddar cheese,
*   grated*
salt and freshly ground black pepper
*   (optional)*

1 Preheat the oven to Gas Mark 5/190°C/375°F.
2 Cook the macaroni in boiling water until tender (7–10 minutes). Drain.
3 Make up the cheese sauce according to the instructions on the packet. Mix the sauce into the macaroni.
4 Heat the oil in a frying pan and fry the pork, courgettes and broccoli for 10 minutes. Put this mixture into an ovenproof dish. Season with salt and pepper.
5 Spoon the macaroni over the pork and vegetables. Sprinkle with the cheese and cook for 25–30 minutes or until golden.

Variation
This also works well with chicken breast and turkey steak. Remember to adjust the Points.

Macaroni Pork

Hearty Chicken Casserole

3 Points per serving

11½ Total Points per recipe

225 Calories per serving

4 Servings

Freezing recommended. Preparation and cooking time: 1½ hours.

This simple casserole is very filling and ideal for those cold winter evenings.

8 chicken drumsticks, skinned

1 large onion, sliced

100 g (3½ oz) carrots, sliced

100 g (3½ oz) courgettes, sliced

3 small potatoes, sliced

1 sachet Colman's Chicken
   Casserole Mix

50 ml (2 fl oz) dry white vermouth
   (optional)

1 Preheat the oven to Gas Mark 4/180°C/350°F

2 Place the chicken, onion, carrots, courgettes and potatoes in an ovenproof casserole dish

3 Mix the contents of the sachet with 425 ml (¾ pint) water. Add the vermouth and pour over the chicken and the vegetables.

4 Cover and cook in the oven for 1 hour or until the chicken is tender.

 ## Mild Chicken Curry

3 Points per serving

12½ Total Points per recipe

200 Calories per serving

4 Servings

Freezing recommended. Preparation and cooking time: 40 minutes.

This mild curry is suitable for all the family. For adults you can add ½ teaspoon chilli powder (or even more if you prefer). Serve the curry with plain boiled rice or pitta bread and low-fat plain yogurt. The curry goes particularly well with Cucumber Raita (page 68). Remember to add on the Points.

1 tablespoon vegetable oil

1 onion, sliced

1 teaspoon cumin seeds

1 red pepper, de-seeded and sliced

2 garlic cloves, crushed

225 g (8 oz) canned tomatoes

1 teaspoon turmeric

2 teaspoons ground coriander

450 g (1 lb) skinless chicken breast,
   cubed

300 ml (½ pint) chicken stock

2 teaspoons garam masala

salt

1 Heat the oil and fry the onion, cumin seeds, red pepper and garlic for 5 minutes.

2 Add the tomatoes, turmeric, salt and ground coriander. Mix thoroughly.

3 Add the chicken and continue stirring for 5 minutes.

4 Add the stock. Cover and simmer gently for a further 20 minutes or until the chicken has cooked.

5 Stir in the garam masala and simmer for 2 minutes.

Variation

Try cubes of Quorn™ and vegetable stock for a vegetarian option. Points per serving will be 2. Calories per serving will be 175.

Tagliatelle Carbonara

6½ Points per serving
27 Total Points per recipe
400 Calories per serving
4 Servings

Freezing not recommended. Preparation and cooking time: 15 minutes.
Ricotta cheese is the basis for this recipe. It's low in Points, but very tasty.

125 g (4½ oz) ricotta cheese
1 egg
200 ml (7 fl oz) skimmed milk
400 g (14 oz) packet fresh tagliatelle
100 g (3½ oz) smoked ham, cut into
    squares
basil leaves (optional)
freshly ground black pepper

1 Mix together the ricotta cheese, egg and skimmed milk in a bowl.
2 Cook the tagliatelle as directed on the packet, and then drain.
3 Return the pasta to the pan while it is still very hot and add the ham. Mix, then add the egg and cheese mixture.
4 Stir well over a low heat to cook the egg gently. Make sure that the sauce has coated all the pasta.
5 Serve with freshly ground black pepper and a few basil leaves, if using.

Cook's tips
Lightly cooked egg should not be served to any vulnerable groups, e.g. children, the elderly or those who are ill.
    Tagliatelle flavoured with garlic and herbs is ideal for this dish.

Sausage Casserole

4 Points per serving
22½ Total Points per recipe
190 Calories per serving
6 Servings

Freezing recommended. Preparation time: 5 minutes + 1 hour cooking.
With this recipe you can cook your whole meal in the oven with a minimum of fuss – simply put in some jacket potatoes at the same time as the casserole. This is a definite favourite with children.

450 g (1 lb) reduced-fat pork sausages,
    uncooked
450 g (1 lb) carrots, sliced
1 large onion, sliced
425 g (15 oz) canned tomatoes
425 g (15 oz) canned oxtail soup

1 Preheat the oven to Gas Mark 8/230°C/450°F.
2 Place the sausages, carrots and onion in an ovenproof casserole dish.
3 Add the canned tomatoes and oxtail soup and cover with cooking foil or a lid.
4 Cook for 1 hour.

Cook's tip
Frozen carrots could easily be used in this recipe. This recipe is for six portions, but if this is too much for your family, freeze some for later on.

Weight Watchers tip
This is lovely served with a medium jacket potato to soak up the delicious gravy – remember to add 2½ Points or 150 Calories for the potato.

Variations
Any vegetables can be added, but swede or turnip is very good. Try different flavours of low-fat sausages for a change – you can even use vegetarian sausages and replace the oxtail soup with vegetable soup. In this case you will only need to cook it for about 30 minutes.

Bacon Ratatouille

4½ Points per serving

9 Total Points per recipe

235 Calories per serving

2 Servings

Freezing not recommended. Preparation and cooking time: 10 minutes.
That lovely smell of bacon and the sunny taste of vegetables will put the sun into the bleakest day!

4 rashers lean back bacon
398 g can ratatouille

1 Preheat the grill to medium.
2 Grill the bacon until not quite crisp.
3 Put the ratatouille in a saucepan and heat.
4 Cut the bacon into bite-sized pieces and add this to the pan. Serve.

Variation
Try turkey rashers for an even lower-fat option. Calories would be 205 per serving.

Spicy Pork Fillets

1½ Points per serving

5½ Total Points per recipe

110 Calories per serving

4 Servings

Freezing not recommended. Preparation time: 10 minutes + 30 minutes marinating + 30 minutes cooking.
This is an easy spicy dish best served with boiled rice and Spicy Tomato Salad (page 68).

350 g (12 oz) pork fillet, trimmed of
*   fat and sliced*

For the marinade
4 tablespoons soy sauce
2 tablespoons water
2 spring onions, chopped finely
1 teaspoon ground ginger
1 garlic clove, crushed
salt and freshly ground black pepper

1 Mix the soy sauce, water, spring onions, ginger and garlic in a shallow ovenproof casserole. Season to taste.
2 Add the pork fillet slices and marinate for at least 30 minutes in the fridge, turning occasionally.
3 Preheat the oven to Gas Mark 4/180°C/ 350°F.
4 Bake the pork with its marinade, uncovered, on the middle shelf for 30 minutes.

Cook's tip
Try to marinate the meat overnight in the fridge if possible. This makes it very tender and more flavoursome.

Weight Watchers tip
Make sure you remove all fat from the meat before marinating – this will keep the Points low. If serving with a medium portion of boiled rice, add 3 Points or 80 Calories – the salad is Point-free!

Variation
Pork loin steaks can be used instead of pork fillet.

Fruity Turkey

3 Points per serving

11 Total Points per recipe

230 Calories per serving

4 Servings

Freezing recommended. Preparation time: 10 minutes + 1½ hours cooking. This combination of fruit and spice provides the strong flavours that turkey needs to liven it up. It's a great dish for Christmas if you don't want to cook a whole turkey.

4 × 100 g (3½ oz) turkey breast fillets

2 small onions, chopped

400 g (14 oz) canned tomatoes

2 medium bananas, chopped

400g (14 oz) canned peach slices in natural juice

½ teaspoon chilli powder

1 Preheat the oven to Gas Mark 7/220°C/425°F.

2 Place all the ingredients in a casserole, cover with a lid or some cooking foil and bake for 1¼ hours.

3 Remove the cover, stir and cook, uncovered, for the last 15 minutes.

Cook's tip

Make sure the tomato and fruit juice mixture covers the turkey fillets so the fillets do not dry out.

Variations

Canned apricots or pineapple in natural juice could be used instead of peaches or use chicken instead of turkey.

Fruity Turkey

 **Herby Pork**

2½ Points per serving

5½ Total Points per recipe

140 Calories per serving

2 Servings

Freezing not recommended. Preparation time: 10 minutes + 10 minutes cooking.

*225 g (8 oz) pork fillet or lean pork
    steaks, cut into thin strips*
*1 bunch of spring onions, trimmed
    and sliced*
100 g (3½ oz) oyster mushrooms, sliced
1 tablespoon wine vinegar
1 teaspoon honey
1 tablespoon dried sage
green leaf salad, to serve

1 Dry-fry the pork strips for 2–3 minutes.
2 Add the spring onions and stir-fry for a further 2 minutes.
3 Add the oyster mushrooms.
4 Add the wine vinegar, honey and dried sage and cook for 5 minutes.
5 Serve on a small leaf salad.

 Bacon Chops with Cumberland Sauce

4½ Points per serving

18 Total Points per recipe

225 Calories per serving

4 Servings

Freezing not recommended. Preparation and cooking time: 15 minutes. Cumberland sauce adds a special touch to meat and makes it ideal for entertaining. The fresh orange and zest give a wonderful citrus flavour, but for quickness you can use 50 ml (2 fl oz) of unsweetened orange juice from a carton.

*4 × 75 g (2¾ oz) bacon chops, trimmed
    of all fat.*

For the sauce
150 g (5½ oz) redcurrant jelly
*finely grated zest and juice of 1 large
    orange*
½ teaspoon Worcestershire sauce
a dash of cayenne pepper

1 Put all the suace ingredients in a non-stick pan and heat gently, stirring continuously, until the jelly has melted.
2 Simmer for 10 minutes.
3 While the sauce is cooking, grill the bacon chops for 5 minutes on each side until done. Serve with the sauce poured over them.

Cook's tips
This works well with either smoked or unsmoked bacon chops.

When grating the orange zest, be careful to not grate any white pith as this will make the sauce bitter.

The sauce can be made in advance and kept in the fridge for up to 5 days in a screwtop jar.

Weight Watchers tip
Serve with a medium jacket potato and a green vegetable; add 2½ Points or 150 Calories.

Variation
The sauce is great served with other grilled meats such as turkey.

Stir-fried Beef **Page 96**
Herby Pork

Springtime Lamb

5 Points per serving
19½ Total Points per recipe
305 Calories per serving
4 Servings

Freezing recommended. Preparation time: 30 minutes + 1 hour cooking.

450 g (1 lb) Healthy Eating lean lamb, cubed
1 large onion, chopped
600 ml (1 pint) fresh lamb stock, or stock made with a herb stock cube
450 g (1 lb) potatoes, peeled and chopped
225 g (8 oz) frozen mixed vegetables

1 Heat a non-stick pan and, without adding any oil, fry the cubed lamb until brown.
2 Add the chopped onion and cook for 3–4 minutes. Make sure the onion doesn't burn.
3 Add the stock and then the potatoes. Simmer for approximately 1 hour until the potatoes and meat are cooked. Add the vegetables and serve when the vegetables are just cooked.

Sausage Risotto

8 Points per serving
32 Total Points per recipe
445 Calories per serving
4 Servings

Freezing recommended. Preparation time: 15 minutes + 30 minutes cooking.
An old favourite with a new look.

1 large onion
450 g (1 lb) reduced-fat sausages
225 g (8 oz) long-grain rice
300 ml (½ pint) stock
400 g (14 oz) canned chopped tomatoes with herbs
salt and freshly ground black pepper

1 Cut the onion into 8. Separate out the petals.
2 Dry-fry the sausages until lightly brown and cut into quarters.
3 Add the onion and cook gently for 2–3 minutes.
4 Add the long-grain rice and stock, and season to taste. Bring to the boil.
5 Add the tomatoes and simmer for 25–30 minutes.

Variation
This recipe could also be made with vegetarian sausages and vegetable stock.

Welshman's Cottage Pie

6 Points per serving
24½ Total Points per recipe
295 Calories per serving
4 Servings

Freezing: recommended. Preparation time: 20 minutes + 30–35 minutes cooking.
With the daffodils on the table there will be a warm welcome from everybody for this dish.

450 g (1 lb) potatoes, peeled and cut into small pieces
225 g (8 oz) leeks, chopped
450 g (1 lb) lean minced lamb
1 onion, finely chopped
300 ml (½ pint) stock
200 g (7 oz) canned chopped tomatoes

1 Preheat the oven to Gas Mark 6/200°C/400°F.
2 Boil the potatoes until nearly cooked. Add the leeks and cook until soft.
3 Drain and mash the potatoes and leeks together.
4 Dry-fry the minced lamb and add the onion. Cook for 5 minutes.
5 Add the stock and tomatoes and transfer to a large ovenproof dish.
6 Top with leek and potato mixture and cook in oven for 30–35 minutes until the top is brown and crispy.

Cook's tip
This dish can be prepared in advance and kept overnight in the refrigerator. Cook in the oven at the same temperature as above, but for 40 minutes.

Crunchy Turkey Napoletana

10 Points per serving

41 Total Points per recipe

610 Calories per serving

4 Servings

Freezing not recommended. Preparation and cooking time: 30 minutes.

Using a ready-prepared sauce can save you so much work – just hide the empty jar and the family need never know!

225 g (8 oz) tagliatelle or other dried
    pasta
550 g pack fresh breaded turkey
    escalopes (you'll get four in a pack)
2 teaspoons oil
300 g jar Heinz Tomato Frito (see tip)
1 teaspoon dried Herbes de Provence
salt and freshly ground black pepper

To garnish

4 teaspoons finely grated parmesan
    cheese
1 small lemon, quartered

1 Cook the pasta in plenty of boiling salted water for 15 minutes, or according to pack instructions. Drain well.

2 While the pasta is cooking, brush the turkey escalopes with oil and grill for 10 minutes on each side, or until cooked through.

3 Heat the sauce to simmering point, stir in the herbs and season with salt and pepper.

4 Arrange the pasta on four heated plates and top with the sauce.

5 Add the escalopes and garnish with parmesan cheese and lemon wedges.

Cook's tips

Heinz Tomato Frito is made from sieved tomatoes with lightly fried onions and a touch of garlic and is ideal for serving over pasta. It's available from most major supermarkets, but if you can't find it, substitute passata, (which is also made from sieved tomatoes), either plain or flavoured with onion and garlic.

Although cheap to make, this is good enough to serve at a dinner party. For extra colour and a really pretty effect, (and if you happen to have it handy), add a sprig of fresh basil to each serving.

Bean, Ham and Tattie Hot-Pot

3½ Points per serving

13 Total Points per recipe

165 Calories per serving

4 Servings

Freezing not recommended. Preparation and cooking time: 15 minutes.

This can go from stove to table in almost less time than it takes to read the recipe. Men love it, kids love it, and it's low in both Calories and fat!

550 g can new potatoes, drained and
    halved
420 g can Weight Watchers from
    Heinz Baked Beans
160 g pack cooked ham cubes
2 teaspoons Worcestershire sauce,
    or to taste
salt and freshly ground black pepper

1 Put the potatoes, beans and ham cubes into a flameproof casserole and heat thoroughly.

2 Add Worcestershire sauce and seasoning to taste, and serve piping hot.

Cook's tip

This can, of course, be made with fresh potatoes, boiled, drained and cut into bite-size pieces, but this would obviously take longer, and the canned potatoes work very well. If you do prefer to use fresh ones, mix them very gently once they have been added to the hot-pot, to avoid breaking them up.

Lamb Steaks with Mint

4 Points per serving

8½ Total Points per recipe

130 Calories per serving

2 Servings

Freezing not recommended. Preparation and cooking time: 15 minutes.
Lamb is my very favourite meat and in this dish the tangy taste of yogurt with mint is wonderful.

150 ml pot low-fat plain yogurt

1 tablespoon dried mint

2 lean lamb steaks (100 g/3½ oz each)

2 tablespoons dried breadcrumbs

1 Preheat the grill.

2 Combine the yogurt and mint.

3 Grill the lamb steaks on one side.

4 Spread the uncooked side with the yogurt mixture and sprinkle with breadcrumbs.

5 Return to the grill. Take care not to burn the topping. Serve when golden and crispy.

Stir-fried Beef

5 Points per serving

20 Total Points per recipe

250 Calories per serving

4 Servings

Freezing recommended. Preparation and cooking time: 15 minutes + 30 minutes marinating.
A delicious oriental dish for special occasions.

3 tablespoons soy sauce

1 tablespoon dry sherry

450 g (1 lb) rump steak, cut into thin strips

Lamb Steaks with Mint

Pork aux Pommes

 **10 Minute Chicken Risotto**

2 tablespoons vegetable oil

1 leek, sliced thinly into rings

1 green pepper, de-seeded and cut into chunks

2.5 cm (1-inch) piece of root ginger, peeled and sliced into thin strips

75 g (2¾ oz) bean sprouts

2 large tomatoes, cut into wedges

salt and freshly ground black pepper

1 Mix together the soy sauce and sherry. Coat the beef well with the mixture and leave to marinate for 30 minutes.

2 Drain the beef, reserving the marinade.

3 Heat the oil in a wok until hot and stir-fry the beef for 2–3 minutes over a high heat. Remove with a slotted spoon and keep warm.

4 Add the leek, pepper and ginger and stir-fry for 4 minutes. Next add the marinade. Return the beef to the pan and add the bean sprouts. Cook for 2–3 minutes until the vegetables are cooked but crisp. Season to taste. Serve immediately with the tomato wedges.

Weight Watchers tip

Serve on a bed of boiled rice. Remember to add on the Points.

Variation

Try strips of boneless chicken or turkey. Points per serving with chicken will be 3½ and with turkey 3. Calories per serving for both will be 230.

4½ Points per serving

9 Total Points per recipe

175 Calories per serving

2 Servings

Freezing recommended. Preparation and cooking time:15–20 minutes.

So simple I don't know why I didn't think of it before. Pork is available as lean cuts these days, so it's easy to incorporate it into a wide range of family favourites.

2 medium lean pork steaks or chops

1 unpeeled red apple, cored and sliced

1 unpeeled green apple, cored and sliced

2 tablespoons lemon juice

salt and freshly ground black pepper

1 Dry-fry the pork steaks for 5–10 minutes, depending on their size. Place on a plate.

2 Put the apples in the pan with the lemon juice.

3 Put the pork steaks on top and cover the pan with its lid or some foil. Season to taste.

4 Cook gently until the apple has softened and the pork is cooked.

5½ Points per serving

11 Total Points per recipe

340 Calories per serving

2 Servings

Freezing recommended. Preparation and cooking time: 10 minutes.

This couldn't be simpler to make. It's a great way to use up leftover chicken, and makes a really quick light lunch or supper dish.

340 g pack Tesco frozen Vegetable Rice,

600 ml (1 pint) chicken stock made with a stock cube

175 g (6 oz) cooked skinless chicken, cut into bite-size pieces

1 teaspoon dried Herbes de Provence

salt and freshly ground black pepper

2 teaspoons parmesan cheese, grated finely, to garnish

1 Cook the rice in chicken stock (instead of water), according to the packet instructions. Drain well.

2 Mix in the chicken and herbs and season to taste with salt and pepper.

3 Reheat gently before serving. Garnish with the grated parmesan.

Variation

This works equally with cooked ham. Safeway Cooked Ham Cubes come in a 160 g pack (that's just under 6 oz).

Beef in Black Bean Sauce

2½ Points per serving

9 Total Points per recipe

125 Calories per serving

4 Servings

Freezing not recommended. Preparation and cooking time: 20 minutes.

This recipe would also be nice with lamb, but, remember to use lean cuts to keep those Points down.

1 teaspoon oil
1 garlic clove, crushed
175 g (6 oz) lean rump steak, sliced
*   thinly*
225 g (8 oz) pack of fresh or frozen
*   stir-fry vegetables*
150 g (5½ oz) jar black bean sauce

1 Heat the oil in large pan or wok and fry the garlic for 1 minute.

2 Add half the beef and cook for a few seconds, then add the rest (see tip). Don't overcook the beef – fry for 3–4 minutes depending how you like your beef cooked.

3 Add the vegetables and stir-fry until just cooked.

4 Pour in the black bean sauce and heat through.

Cook's tip

If you put too much meat into a hot wok it will lower the temperature of the wok. The meat won't seal and the juices will run out; this means the meat will stew rather than fry.

Turkey Scaloppine al Limone

2½ Points per serving

10 Total Points per recipe

155 Calories per serving

4 Servings

Freezing recommended. Preparation and cooking time: 20 minutes.

Perfect for a special dinner party, this dish is traditionally made with escalopes of veal, but it works just as well with the thin turkey breast steaks which are now available in most large supermarkets. It's so simple, so quick, and so low in both Calories and fat!

450 g (1 lb) pack thin-cut unbreaded
*   turkey breast steaks (you'll find 4*
*   in a pack)*
150 ml (¼ pint) chicken stock (made
*   with ½ stock cube)*
150 ml (¼ pint) dry white wine
juice of 1 lemon + 4 thin lemon slices,
*   halved*
1 teaspoon dried Italian herbs
2 teaspoons sauce flour (see tip)
salt and freshly ground black pepper
2 tablespoons chopped fresh parsley,
*   to garnish*

1 Cut each steak in half, and beat flat with a rolling pin.

2 Put the chicken stock, white wine and lemon juice in a large non-stick frying pan and bring to simmering point.

3 Add the turkey steaks, lemon slices, seasoning and herbs and poach the steaks gently for 15 minutes, turning once during cooking.

4 Remove the steaks and lemon slices from the pan with a slotted spoon and keep warm. Remove the pan from the heat.

5 Put the sauce flour in a small bowl, and stir in enough of the liquid from the pan to make a smooth paste. Stir the paste into the remaining liquid in the pan to form a thick, smooth sauce.

6 Return the turkey and lemon slices to the pan, reheat without boiling and serve garnished with fresh chopped parsley.

Cook's tip

Sauce flour is comparatively new on the market, and has been milled specially to reduce the risk of lumpiness. It can also be used in stews or casseroles to thicken gravy without adding any extra colour. It's available from Sainsbury's under their own brand label. If you don't have a Sainsbury's nearby, or can't find the flour, mix 2 teaspoons cornflour with a little cold water to form a paste, and stir the paste into the sauce. Bring to the boiling point, and keep stirring till sauce thickens.

Weight Watchers tip

You could use skinless chicken breast fillets, but bear in mind that turkey is lower in fat.

Shepherd's Bean Bake

6 Points per serving

24 Total Points per recipe

315 Calories per serving

4 Servings

Freezing recommended. Preparation time: 20 minutes + 25 minutes cooking.

Quick, easy and economical too – this is just the thing for a midweek family supper.

450 g (1 lb) potatoes
350 g (12 oz) lean minced lamb
1 onion, chopped finely
200 ml (7 fl oz) lamb stock, (made with ½ Knorr cube)
2 teaspoons brown gravy granules
420 g can Weight Watchers from Heinz Baked Beans
salt and freshly ground black pepper

1 Preheat the oven to Gas Mark 6/200°C/ 400°F.

2 Boil the potatoes until tender. When they are done drain and mash them, and season to taste.

3 Brown the mince in a non-stick pan for 2 or 3 minutes, stirring with a wooden spoon. Drain off any excess fat.

4 Add the chopped onion, stock and gravy granules, and bring to the boil. Lower the heat and simmer gently for 15 minutes.

5 Add the baked beans and season to taste.

6 Put in an ovenproof dish and top with the mashed potatoes.

7 Bake for 25 minutes and, if necessary, finish off by browning under a hot grill.

Cook's tip

This is very simple and quick to prepare, because you can make the meat and bean mixture while the potatoes are boiling.

Weight Watchers tip

The bake would brown quicker if the top was brushed with a little butter or margarine, but then again, you'd be adding extra Calories and precious Points. It should brown without the added fat, but oven temperatures can vary, so it may be necessary to finish it off under a hot grill. Have a look a few minutes before it's done just to check.

Variation

Use lean minced beef instead of lamb. Points will be 5. Calories will increase to 330 per serving.

Super Simple Lasagne Bolognese

6 Points per serving

24 Total Points per recipe

365 Calories per serving

4 Servings

Freezing recommended. Preparation time: 20 minutes + 30 minutes baking.

If you've always thought lasagne too fiddly to make, (not to mention too fattening!), try this easy low-Points version.

350 g (12 oz) extra-lean minced beef
400 g (14 oz) canned chopped tomatoes with peppers and onions
½ teaspoon dried garlic powder
1 teaspoon dried Herbes de Provence or Italian dried herbs
8 sheets no-need-to-precook lasagne
salt and freshly ground black pepper

For the sauce

25 g (1 oz) plain flour, sifted, or sauce flour (see tip)
295 g can Weight Watchers from Heinz Mushroom Soup
50 g (1¾ oz) Shape Mature Cheddar cheese, grated

1 Preheat the oven to Gas Mark 6/200°C/ 400°F.

2 Brown the mince in a large non-stick frying pan for 2 or 3 minutes, stirring with a wooden spatula.

3 Mix in the tomatoes, seasoning, garlic powder and herbs and bring to simmering point. Cook on a medium heat for 5 minutes.

4 Put half the meat mixture into the bottom of an ovenproof dish, (preferably rectangular), and top with 4 sheets of the lasagne.

5 Add the rest of the meat mixture and the remaining sheets of lasagne.

6 Put the flour into a small pan and add one third of the soup. Cook very gently, stirring all the time. Gradually add the rest of the soup until a smooth, thick sauce is obtained.

7 Add the cheese and stir until thoroughly blended in. Season with salt and pepper.

8 Pour over the lasagne and bake for 30 minutes. If necessary, brown under a hot grill before serving.

Weight Watchers tip

This is low in Calories because it uses extra lean mince. If you see any fat in the pan when you brown the meat, blot it off with a wodge of kitchen paper. The basic white sauce is also very low in fat. It needs to be well-stirred to avoid lumps. Sainsbury's own-label sauce flour is very good for the job, but if you are using ordinary plain flour, make sure that you sieve it first.

 ## Chilli con Carne

3 Points per serving

12 Total Points per recipe

165 Calories per serving

4 Servings

Freezing recommended. Preparation and cooking time: 40 minutes.

This classic Mexican dish is lovely served with pitta bread or a jacket potato and some low-fat plain yogurt. A real winter warmer.

250 g (9 oz) lean minced beef (less than 5% fat)
2 onions, chopped
205 g canned tomatoes
205 g canned Weight Watchers from Heinz baked beans
205 g canned kidney beans, drained
1 tablespoon tomato purée
½ teaspoon chilli powder

1 Heat the minced beef gently in a large, non-stick saucepan. This will release the fat in the meat and prevent the meat from sticking.

2 Add the onions and cook until all the meat is coloured and there is no pink showing.

3 Add the rest of the ingredients and simmer gently for 15 minutes.

Cook's tip

Make this dish the day before you need it and store it overnight in the fridge. You'll find that this really helps the flavours blend together. It also means that you can produce a very quick meal; simply re-heat the chilli con carne for 10 minutes until piping hot.

Weight Watchers tip

If serving with a medium pitta bread, or a jacket potato add 2½ Points.

Variations

Try minced lamb or turkey, or use minced Quorn™ for a vegetarian dish. Points per serving with lamb will be 4 (or 215 Calories); with turkey 2½ (or 160 Calories) and with Quorn™ 2 (or 145 Calories).

 ## Lancashire Hot-pot

 ## Chicken Cordon Bleu

4½ Points per serving
18 Total Points per recipe
295 Calories per serving
4 Servings

Freezing recommended. Preparation time: 15 minutes + 1½ hours cooking.
An old-fashioned favourite given a new-fashioned look, this is a wonderfully warming winter filler that's low in both Calories and fat, because it's made with a very lean cut of lamb.

600 g (1 lb 5 oz) potatoes, peeled and sliced thinly
450 g (1 lb) frozen stewpack, or casserole, vegetables
250 g pack thin-cut Healthy Eating lamb leg steaks (you'll get 6 in a pack)
300 ml (½ pint) lamb stock made with a stock cube
1 tablespoon gravy granules
salt and freshly ground black pepper

1 Preheat the oven to Gas Mark 5/190°C/375°F.
2 Arrange a layer of potatoes in the bottom of an ovenproof dish, and season with salt and pepper.
3 Top with a layer of vegetables and 2 steaks, halved crossways. Season.
4 Repeat the layers as above, seasoning each one and finishing with a layer of potatoes.
5 Thicken the stock with the gravy granules, add to the casserole, cover and bake for 1½ hours. Remove the lid for the last ½ hour to allow the potatoes to brown.

5 Points per serving
19 Total Points per recipe
230 Calories per serving
4 Servings

Freezing recommended (see tip). Preparation time: 15 minutes + 30 minutes cooking.
This makes a lovely dish for entertaining. With its festive-looking red sauce and brilliant green herb garnish, this would be particularly appropriate served some time over the Christmas holidays. You will also need some cocktail sticks.

4 × 150 g (5½ oz) skinless boneless chicken breast fillets
2 × 25 g (1 oz) slices of lean honey-roast ham, halved
4 low-fat cheese slices
400 g (14 oz) canned chopped tomatoes with basil
salt and freshly ground black pepper
basil or parsley sprigs, to garnish

1 Preheat the oven to Gas Mark 5/190°C/375°F.
2 Take the chicken fillets and a sharp knife. Each fillet has a natural 'pocket' in the flesh. Find this and, with the knife, gently enlarge it so that it will hold more filling.
3 Wrap each piece of ham in a cheese single, and use to fill the chicken 'pockets.' Press the edges of the chicken flesh firmly together and, if necessary, secure with wooden cocktail sticks.

4 Put the chicken breasts into an ovenproof dish and pour on the chopped tomatoes. Season with salt and pepper.
5 Bake for 30 minutes. Remove the cocktail sticks, and serve each chicken breast garnished with sprigs of basil or parsley.

Cook's tip
To freeze, prepare the dish up to the end of step 4 and then freeze.

Cranberry and Orange Glazed Gammon Steaks

6 Points per serving

24½ Total Points per recipe

260 Calories per serving

4 Servings

Freezing recommended. Preparation and cooking time: 15 minutes.
These make an ideal Christmas Eve or Boxing Night supper, and go particularly well with jacket potatoes and a crisp green salad.

1 orange
4 × 150 g (5½ oz) lean gammon steaks

4 tablespoons cranberry sauce
½ teaspoon ground cloves

1 Without peeling the orange cut 4 good slices. Take out any pips and halve the slices to form half moon shapes.

2 Grill the gammon steaks under a medium heat for 5 minutes on each side, or until cooked through.

3 While the steaks are cooking, warm the cranberry sauce with the cloves.

4 Spread each steak with 1 tablespoon of the warmed jelly, and top each with 2 orange half moons.

5 Turn up the heat, flash the steaks under grill for 3 or 4 seconds and serve immediately.

Cook's tip

The orange half moons help to make this a very festive-looking dish. If you intend to eat them, use a peeled orange when preparing the slices.

Weight Watchers tip

Don't forget to add extra Points for the jacket potatoes. A 225 g (8 oz) potato will cost you 2½ Points or 150 Calories.

Cranberry and Orange Glazed Gammon Steaks

Sunset Oven-Cooked Pork

4½ Points per serving

17½ Total Points per recipe

155 Calories per serving

4 Servings

Freezing recommended. Preparation time: 15 minutes + 20 minutes cooking. Lean pork is very low in fat if it's well trimmed, but it does tend to be rather dry. This way of cooking adds both flavour and moisture. It makes an excellent family supper or 'budget' dinner party dish.

1 medium orange
400 g (14 oz) pack lean thin-cut pork loin steaks
400 g (14 oz) canned chopped tomatoes with peppers and onions
1 teaspoon dried mixed herbs
salt and freshly-ground black pepper

1 Without peeling the orange, cut 4 good slices. Take out any pips and halve the slices to form half moon shapes.
2 Preheat the oven to Gas Mark 5/190°C/375°F.
3 Put the pork loin steaks, overlapping, into an ovenproof dish.
4 Add the chopped tomatoes, season to taste with salt and pepper and sprinkle with the herbs.
5 Top with the orange slices and bake for 20 minutes.

Cook's tip

The orange 'half moons' will soften in the cooking. They also look very attractive, so there is no need for an added garnish.

Weight Watchers tip

This dish cries out to be served with mashed potatoes. A 2 scoop serving will give just 2 Points or 100 Calories per serving. It's also good with any green vegetable, particularly cabbage or fine green beans, which are Point-free.

Variation

For an even tastier dish, (particularly for a dinner party), mix in 4 tablespoons apple sauce. This will add 15 Calories to each serving. Points will remain the same.

 **Irish Stew**

3 Points per serving

13 Total Points per recipe

205 Calories per serving

4 Servings

Freezing recommended. Preparation time: 10 minutes + 30 minutes cooking.

Traditionally this is made with the cheaper cuts of lamb, such as scrag end, but these can be very high in Calories and fat, so choose the leanest meat you can find. Tesco's Healthy Eating diced lamb is particularly good, as it contains less than 5% fat and cooks very quickly.

400 g (14 oz) very lean lamb, diced
300 ml (½ pint) stock made with a lamb
    or chicken stock cube
3 carrots, sliced thinly
2 onions, sliced finely
1 tablespoon white thickening granules
    (see tip)
salt and freshly ground black pepper
2 tablespoons chopped fresh parsley,
    to garnish

1 Heat a heavy-bottomed non-stick pan and brown the meat, stirring with a wooden spoon, so that it browns evenly.

2 Add the stock and vegetables and bring to the boil.

3 Lower the heat, cover the pan, and simmer gently for 30 minutes until the vegetables and meat are tender.

4 Remove the pan from the heat, season well with salt and pepper, and stir in the thickening granules.

5 Sprinkle with chopped fresh parsley before serving.

Cook's tip

White thickening granules are made by McDougalls and are widely available at supermarkets throughout the country. They're great for thickening stews and casseroles where no added colour is required. If you can't get them, mix 1 tablespoon cornflour with a little cold water to form a paste, and stir this into the cooking liquor. Keep stirring, until it boils and thickens.

 **Beefsteak Romantica**

7 Points per serving

14½ Total Points per recipe

395 Calories per serving

2 Servings

Freezing not recommended. Preparation and cooking time: 20 minutes.

This is a really glamorous, special-occasion meal for two, and is both quick and simple to make. Light the candles, get him to pour the wine, and you're half-way there already!

2 × 125 g (4½ oz) lean fillet steaks
2 × 20 g sachet Crosse and Blackwell's
    Madeira Wine Sauce
2 × 50 g (1¾ oz) slices French bread
25 g (1 oz) low-fat Ardennes pâté
    (see tip)
freshly ground black pepper

1 Grill the steaks for 5–6 minutes each side, depending on how you like them.

2 While they're cooking, make up the sauce according to the packet instructions.

3 Toast the bread on one side only. Spread the untoasted side with the pâté.

4 Pop under the grill for a couple of seconds, just to warm it through.

5 Top with the steaks, sprinkle with pepper and pour on the sauce before serving.

Cook's tip

If you can't find a low-fat Ardennes pâté, (Tesco do one), any low-fat pâté will do. If the worst comes to the worst, (which it shouldn't, as most supermarkets do have

low-fat varieties), use a standard pâté and
mix it half-and-half with low-fat spread.

Variation
For an extra touch of glamour, garnish
each serving with 3 or 4 canned asparagus
spears (heated and drained).

Think this section is only for vegetarians? Then think again. You don't need to follow a vegetarian diet to enjoy Speedy Chow Mein, Mushroom Stroganoff, Crunchy Vegetable Pizza or Peanut Peppers. And you don't need to know how to cook with obscure and unusual vegetables to indulge in Creamy Pasta or Quick Mediterranean Vegetable Risotto.

The '5 a day' message is a familiar one, so use this chapter to help you get up to speed. Remember, vegetables are rich in vitamin C and other vital nutrients. They're also full of fibre which means you feel fuller sooner and end up eating less – and that helps keep the Points down.

Most of the recipes in this chapter will double up as side dishes; Pear And Watercress Salad, for example, is a very refreshing accompaniment. Remember, whatever way you choose to serve them, each recipe here will help you keep to a healthy weight-loss eating plan.

vegetarian

main meals

Speedy Chow Mein

Ⓥ

3½ Points per serving

10 Total Points per recipe

205 Calories per serving

❸ Servings

Freezing not recommended. Preparation and cooking time: 15 minutes.
When you fancy a quick Chinese but can't afford the local take-away, create this speedy noodle dish which needs no accompaniments.

85 g packet instant noodles

2 teaspoons sesame oil

1 teaspoon crushed ginger

3 tablespoons light soy sauce

420 g canned sweetcorn

250 g (9 oz) frozen Chinese vegetables

salt and freshly ground black pepper

1 Cook the noodles in lightly salted boiling water. Drain.

2 Heat the oil in a wok or frying pan and add the ginger. Stir-fry for a minute.

3 Mix in the soy sauce and all the vegetables. Stir-fry until just cooked.

4 Gently stir in the noodles, adjust the seasoning and serve.

Cook's tip

Often instant noodles come with soup mix sachets. This is fine – just save the powdered soup mix for another day.

Quorn Mega Burger

Ⓥ

6½ Points per serving

370 Calories per serving

❶ Serving

Freezing not recommended. Preparation and cooking time: 15 minutes.
I've been pleasantly surprised by these burgers. They taste good, cook quickly and are much lower in Points than meat versions. You can make it as mega as you like by adding mountains of fresh salad vegetables.

2 frozen or chilled Quorn burgers

1 medium seeded burger bun

crisp lettuce leaves

2.5 cm (1-inch) piece of cucumber, sliced

2 tomatoes, sliced

1 small carrot, grated

1 low-fat cheese slice

2 teaspoons tomato ketchup

1 teaspoon Weight Watchers from Heinz low-fat mayonnaise

1 Cook the burgers according to the instructions on the packet.

2 Cut the roll in half and fill it with half the lettuce, cucumber, tomato and grated carrot.

3 Place one burger on top of this and repeat the layers.

4 Place the cheese slice over this and then flavour with the ketchup and dressing. Replace the top of the roll.

 ## Pasta with Red Kidney Beans

Ⓥ

7 Points per serving

28 Total Points per recipe

480 Calories per serving

❹ Servings

Freezing not recommended. Preparation and cooking time: 30 minutes.
A speedy low-fat meal for a hectic day!

300 g (10½ oz) pasta shapes

1 tablespoon vegetable oil

1 onion, sliced thinly

400 g (14 oz) canned chopped tomatoes

1 teaspoon mixed herbs

425 g (15 oz) canned red kidney beans in salted water

75 g (2¾ oz) half-fat Cheddar cheese, grated

salt and freshly ground black pepper

1 Boil the pasta as instructed on the packet and drain.

2 Meanwhile, heat the oil in a large saucepan and gently fry the onion, stirring occasionally, until lightly browned.

3 Add the tomatoes, herbs and the red kidney beans with their liquid. Stir well and season to taste. Simmer for 10 minutes.

4 Mix in the pasta, put on low heat and heat. Serve immediately.

5 Sprinkle on the grated cheese just before serving

Variation

Canned chick-peas can be substituted for the red kidney beans.

Lentil Bolognese

2 Points per serving

8 Total Points per recipe

150 Calories per serving

4 Servings

Freezing recommended. Preparation and cooking time: 40 minutes.

This spicy vegetarian dish is very versatile. It can be served as a thick soup for a starter. Or serve with boiled spaghetti, boiled rice or pitta bread as a main course – yum!

75 g (2¾ oz) red lentils

2 tablespoons vegetable oil

1 onion, chopped finely

2 garlic cloves, crushed

1 cm (½ inch) piece fresh root ginger, peeled and chopped finely

400 g (14 oz) canned chopped tomatoes

1 tablespoon chopped fresh marjoram (or 1 teaspoon dried marjoram)

½ teaspoon paprika

salt

1 Soak the lentils in cold water for 10 minutes. Drain.

2 Meanwhile in a large saucepan bring 450 ml (16 fl oz) water to the boil. Add the drained lentils and bring the mixture back to the boil. Partially cover with a lid and simmer for about 20 minutes until the mixture is thick and the lentils soft. If you have a pressure cooker the lentils can be cooked in less than 10 minutes.

3 While the lentils are cooking, heat the oil in a saucepan and gently fry the onion without browning. Add the garlic and ginger, and cook, stirring, for 1 minute.

4 Add the tomatoes, marjoram, paprika and salt. Partially cover with a lid and simmer for 5 minutes.

5 Add this mixture to the cooked lentils, stirring well. Bring to the boil and allow to simmer for a further 5 minutes.

Weight Watchers tip

Lentils are cheap and very nutritious. They provide protein, fibre, vitamins and minerals.

Variation

For a meat option, substitute 450 g (1 lb) extra-lean minced beef for the lentils and omit steps 1 and 2. Add the mince with the tomatoes, marjoram, paprika and salt and cook for 20–30 minutes. The Points will be 4½ per serving and the Calories 225 per serving.

Spicy Macaroni Cheese and Mushroom Crumble

5 Points per serving

19 Total Points per recipe

280 Calories per serving

4 Servings

Freezing recommended (see tip). Preparation time: 20 minutes + 20 minutes cooking.

225 g (8 oz) quick-cook macaroni

125 g (4½ oz) button mushrooms, halved

295 g can Weight Watchers from Heinz Tomato Soup

a pinch of cayenne

2 tomatoes, sliced

25 g (1 oz) fresh wholemeal breadcrumbs

50 g (1¾ oz) Shape Mature Cheddar cheese, grated

salt and freshly ground black pepper

1 Preheat the oven to Gas Mark 6/200°C/400°F.

2 Cook the macaroni in plenty of boiling salted water for 5 minutes or according to the packet instructions. Drain well.

3 Mix in the mushrooms and tomato soup and season with salt, pepper and cayenne.

4 Transfer to an ovenproof dish, top with sliced tomatoes and again season.

5 Mix the breadcrumbs with the cheese. Sprinkle on top and bake for 20 minutes.

Cook's tip

This is best frozen without the tomato and crumble topping.

Cheesy Vegetables

(V)

½ Point per serving

2½ Total Points per recipe

105 Calories per serving

4 Servings

Freezing not recommended. Preparation and cooking time: 25 minutes.

This fast and tasty dish can be served as an accompaniment or as a main course with warm crusty french bread. Remember to add on the Points.

3 carrots, sliced

1 cauliflower, divided into florets

100 g (3½ oz) broccoli florets

50 g (1¾ oz) frozen peas

40 g (1½ oz) sachet Colman's Cheese
    Sauce

1 teaspoon Dijon mustard

salt and freshly ground black pepper

1 Cook the carrots in boiling water for 3 minutes.

2 Add the remaining vegetables. Cook until the vegetables are just tender. Drain and put the vegetables in a large flameproof dish. Cover and keep warm.

3 Make up the cheese sauce as directed on the packet. Stir in the mustard and the seasoning.

4 Pour the sauce over the vegetables and mix gently.

5 Grill under medium heat for 5 minutes. Serve immediately.

Variation

Any fresh vegetables can be used.

Crusty Cauliflower Cheese Grill

(V)

7 Points per serving

14 Total Points per recipe

275 Calories per serving

2 Servings

Freezing recommended. Preparation and cooking time: 25 minutes.

A new variation on an old favourite. This makes a nice cheap midweek supper.

1 medium cauliflower, cut into florets

For the sauce

25 g (1 oz)) polyunsaturated margarine

25 g (1 oz) plain flour

300 ml (½ pint) skimmed milk

50 g (1¾ oz) Shape Mature Cheddar
    cheese

1 teaspoon Dijon mustard

salt and white pepper

For the crumble topping

25 g (1 oz) fresh wholemeal
    breadcrumbs

15 g (½ oz) Shape Mature Cheddar
    cheese

1 Cook the cauliflower in lightly salted boiling water until just tender. Drain and put into a shallow serving dish. Keep hot.

2 Melt the margarine in a small pan over a moderate heat. Stir in the flour and mix well. Cook for 30 seconds.

3 Slowly add one third of the milk, stirring all the time. Gradually add the rest of the milk, stirring continuously until the sauce thickens.

4 Lower the heat and cook for a further 2 minutes. Stir in the cheese and mustard and season well.

5 Pour the sauce over the cauliflower, top with the breadcrumbs and cheese and brown under a hot grill before serving.

Cook's tips

If you can't be bothered making the sauce from scratch, use a white sauce mix from a packet made up with skimmed milk and add the cheese and mustard.

For non-vegetarians, this makes a delicious accompaniment to meat or fish.

Variation

Make the grill with broccoli instead of cauliflower, or try a mixture of both.

Pancakes Provençale

 ## Crunchy Rice Salad

Ⓥ

1½ Points per serving

6 Total Points per recipe

140 Calories per serving

4 Servings

Freezing not recommended. Preparation and cooking time: 30 minutes.
This is a versatile dish; the filling can be as varied and colourful as you want – remember to alter the Points.

130 g packet pancake mix

For the filling
2 courgettes, sliced
1 red pepper, de-seeded and sliced
200 g (7 oz) canned chopped tomatoes
1 garlic clove, crushed
100 g (3½ oz) mushrooms, sliced
salt and freshly ground black pepper

1 Make the pancakes according to the instructions on the packet but make it slightly thicker than instructed to hold the vegetable filling.
2 Put the courgettes, pepper, tomatoes, garlic and mushrooms into a large saucepan.
3 Simmer, uncovered, for about 10 minutes. Stir occasionally.
4 Cover with a lid and cook for a further 5 minutes, stirring. Season to taste.
5 Spoon some mixture into the middle of each pancake. Fold each pancake in half and then in half again to make a cone shape. Serve hot.

Ⓥ

3 Points per serving

12½ Total Points per recipe

220 Calories per serving

4 Servings

Freezing recommended. Preparation and cooking time: 30 minutes.

1 red apple, diced
1 green apple, diced
2 carrots, grated
3 spring onions, sliced
300 g canned peas in water, drained
125 g (4½ oz) long-grain rice, cooked
1 tablespoon fat-free dressing
1 tablespoon raisins

1 Mix all the fruit and vegetables with the rice and dressing. Sprinkle on the raisins and chill.

Pancakes Provençale

 ## Caribbean Chick-peas

 ## Veggie-sausage Cassoulet

Ⓥ

3 Points per serving

12½ Total Points per recipe

130 Calories per serving

❹ Servings

Freezing not recommended. Preparation and cooking time: 20 minutes.
Canned chick-peas make this a quick and easy recipe.

low-fat cooking spray
2 teaspoon mustard seeds
1 large onion, chopped finely
400 g (14 oz) canned chick-peas in
    water, drained
½ teaspoon chilli powder
25 g (1 oz) desiccated coconut
parsley or coriander leaves, to garnish

1 Heat a heavy-based, non-stick frying pan until hot and then spray with 4 sprays of low-fat cooking spray. Add the mustard seeds.

2 When the mustard seeds begin to pop, add the onion and cook until soft. Add a little water if necessary to stop the onion sticking.

3 Add the chick-peas and chilli powder and cook until hot, stirring continuously.

4 Add the coconut, mix well and serve sprinkled with parsley or coriander leaves.

Weight Watchers tip

Serve with a medium pitta bread (add 2½ Points or 150 Calories) and Spicy Tomato Salad (page 68).

Ⓥ

2½ Points per serving

11 Total Points per recipe

170 Calories per serving

❹ Servings

Freezing not recommended. Preparation time: 10 minutes + 30 minutes cooking.
Cassoulet is a bean stew from France prepared with pork or lamb. This version, which contains no meat, tastes just as good.

low-fat cooking spray
2 onions, chopped roughly
1 garlic clove, crushed
250 g (9 oz) packet Quorn sausages
410 g canned tomatoes and herbs
190 g canned butter beans in water,
    drained
190 g canned beans, drained (e.g.
    kidney, cannellini, flageolet or
    haricot)
1 tablespoon tomato purée
1 teaspoon mustard
salt and freshly ground pepper

1 Spray a large, shallow non-stick pan with 4 sprays of low-fat cooking spray and cook the onions, garlic and sausages gently until they start to brown. Add 1 teaspoon water if they start to stick.

2 Add the remainder of the ingredients and mix well. Season.

3 Simmer for 20 minutes and serve.

Cook's tip

Any mustard can be used for this recipe, but a large teaspoon of Dijon mustard is ideal.

Weight Watchers tip

Serve with a medium jacket potato (2½ Points) to soak up the sauce, and some boiled cauliflower.

Variation

Meat or sausages can be used for a non-vegetarian dish. Remember to adjust the Points.

Tomato Rice

V

3 Points per serving

11½ Total Points per recipe

250 Calories per serving

4 Servings

Freezing not recommended. Preparation time: 10 minutes + 25 minutes cooking. This is delicious as a main meal, or served as a side dish with vegetarian sausages or burgers.

low-fat cooking spray
1 onion, chopped
1 green pepper, de-seeded and sliced
225 g (8 oz) button mushrooms, sliced
225 g (8 oz) long-grain rice
400 g (14 oz) canned tomatoes
600 ml (1 pint) vegetable stock made
  with a stock cube
2 tablespoons tomato purée
½ teaspoon mixed herbs
salt and freshly ground black pepper

1 Spray a large, shallow, non-stick pan with 4 sprays of low-fat cooking spray and cook the onion until soft.

2 Add the green pepper, mushrooms and 2 tablespoons water and cook for a further 2 minutes.

3 Add the rice and mix thoroughly.

4 Add the remaining ingredients and bring to the boil stirring continuously.

5 Simmer for 20 minutes, stirring occasionally to prevent sticking.

Cook's tip

Rice varies a great deal in the amount of liquid it will absorb so check the rice is completely cooked before serving. If necessary add a little extra stock or water and continue to cook until it is done.

Weight Watchers tip

This recipe serves 6 as a side dish (2 Points or 165 Calories per serving).

Variations

Add 1 teaspoon chilli powder to spice up the Tomato Rice or, for non-vegetarians, add some cooked chicken before serving, adding the extra Points.

Topatoes

V

4 Points per serving

16 Total Points per recipe

250 Calories per serving

4 Servings

Freezing not recommended. Preparation and cooking time: 1 hour. This is a lovely way to prepare new potatoes. It is especially nice with cold meat.

750 g (1 lb 10 oz) new potatoes, sliced
low-fat cooking spray
350 g (12 oz) tomatoes, sliced thinly
250 g (9 oz) low-fat plain yogurt
2 teaspoons Herbes de Provence
50 g (1¾ oz) Red Leicester cheese,
  grated finely
freshly ground black pepper

1 Preheat the oven to Gas Mark 6/200°C/ 400°F.

2 Bring the potatoes to the boil and cook for 5 minutes.

3 Lightly grease an ovenproof dish with 4 sprays of low-fat cooking spray and use one third of the potatoes to cover the base.

4 Cover with a thin layer of tomatoes and season with black pepper.

5 Repeat the layers, finishing with a layer of overlapping potatoes.

6 Pour the yogurt over the top and sprinkle with the herbs.

7 Finally cover with the cheese and bake in the oven for 30–40 minutes.

Potato Bombes

Ⓥ

1 Point per serving

5 Total Points per recipe

115 Calories per serving

➍ Servings

Freezing not recommended. Preparation time: 30 minutes + 30 minutes cooking. This is great for entertaining: it can be prepared in advance and it makes a colourful addition to any dining table.

450 g (1 lb) potatoes, chopped
½ teaspoon ground nutmeg
2 tablespoons skimmed milk
175 g (6 oz) frozen spinach, thawed
low-fat cooking spray
salt and freshly ground black pepper

1 Preheat the oven to Gas Mark 6/220°C/400°F.
2 Boil the potatoes in lightly salted water until tender. Drain.
3 Mash the potatoes with the nutmeg and the milk.
4 Squeeze the excess water out of the thawed spinach and mix the spinach with the potatoes. Season to taste.
5 Lightly spray four small ovenproof moulds with low-fat cooking spray. Divide the potato mixture between them and bake in the oven for 20 minutes.
6 Run a knife around the moulds to help turn out the potato bombes.

Variations
Curly kale or cabbage and carrots or swede make a nice alternative to spinach.

Sweet and Sour Mushrooms

Ⓥ

1 Point per serving

3½ Total Points per recipe

95 Calories per serving

➍ Servings

Freezing not recommended. Preparation and cooking time: 30 minutes.
The sweet and sour sauces you can now buy are better than home-made and are available in so many varieties. Here I have used a low-Calorie version, and I have spiced it up for those who like it hot!

4 large open-cup mushrooms
400 g (14 oz) jar Uncle Ben's Shanghai
*   Sweet and Sour Sauce*
125 g (4½ oz) canned baby corn,
*   drained and chopped into chunks*
6 spring onions, sliced
125 g (4½ oz) canned bamboo shoots,
*   drained*
½ teaspoon chilli powder (optional)

1 Preheat the oven to Gas Mark 8/230°C/450°F.
2 Place the mushrooms on a non-stick baking tray and bake for 20 minutes.
3 Meanwhile put the sweet and sour sauce in a large saucepan, and add the remainder of the ingredients.
4 Heat thoroughly for 5 minutes, stirring occasionally, until all the ingredients are well blended.
5 Put a mushroom on each serving plate and pile the hot sweet and sour vegetable mixture on top.

Weight Watchers tip
Serve with a medium portion of boiled rice (3 Points or 80 Calories) and soy sauce.

Variation
285 g (10 oz) cubes of tofu (beancurd) could be used instead of the mushrooms in this recipe. The Points per serving will be 2.

Vegetable Pilau Rice

Ⓥ

4 Points per serving

15½ Total Points per recipe

265 Calories per serving

④ Servings

Freezing not recommended. Preparation and cooking time: 30 minutes.

It is best to use mixed vegetables for this delectable rice dish as they make the pilau look very attractive and appetising.

1 tablespoon vegetable oil
½ teaspoon cumin seeds
1 cinnamon stick
2 garlic cloves, sliced
1 tomato, sliced
225 g (8 oz) easy-cook brown rice
200 g (7 oz) frozen mixed vegetables
salt

1 Heat the oil in a medium saucepan and add the spices, garlic and salt.

2 Add the tomato and stir-fry for about 2 minutes.

3 Add the rice and frozen vegetables and stir gently.

4 Add the amount of water given on the rice packet. Bring the mixture to the boil. Lower the heat, cover and cook according to the instructions on the rice packet.

Weight Watchers tip

The advantage of brown rice over white is that brown still has its natural fibre.

Stuffed Aubergines

Ⓥ

2 Points per serving

8 Total Points per recipe

235 Calories per serving

④ Servings

Freezing not recommended. Preparation time: ½ hour + 1 hour cooking.

You don't have to be vegetarian to enjoy this recipe. Try it as a lunch or supper dish and serve with a green salad.

125 g packet savoury rice (see tip)
4 aubergines
225 g (8 oz) mushrooms, chopped
4 tomatoes, chopped roughly
175 g (6 oz) plain cottage cheese, sieved

1 In a non-stick saucepan cook the savoury rice as directed on the packet (normally add water and simmer for 20 minutes).

2 While the rice is cooking, cut the stalk off each aubergine, then slice in half lengthwise. Scoop out the flesh and chop.

3 Preheat the oven to Gas Mark 4/180°C/ 350°F.

4 When the rice is cooked, add the mushrooms, tomatoes and aubergine flesh to the rice mixture and cook for a further 3 minutes, stirring well (add a little stock or water if needed).

5 Add the sieved cottage cheese, and mix thoroughly before piling the mixture into 4 aubergine halves and covering each with its other half.

6 Wrap the aubergines loosely in cooking foil and place on a baking tray.

7 Bake for 45 minutes to 1 hour (depending on the size of the aubergine) until tender.

Cook's tip

Herb-and-garlic-flavoured savoury rice is ideal, but any other sort will do.

The aubergines could also be stuffed whole by simply removing the stalk end, scooping out the flesh and cutting a flat base at the other end for it to stand on. This is best for smaller vegetables.

Variations

Try stuffing other vegetables in the same way – peppers, squash or courgettes, or use some cooked minced meat instead of cottage cheese for a meaty dish! Adjust the Points as necessary.

Crunchy Vegetable Pizza

Ⓥ

3½ Points per serving

15 Total Points per recipe

330 Calories per serving

4 Servings

Freezing recommended for the base only (see tip). Preparation and cooking time: 30 minutes.

This classic dish is quick to make. It can even be cooked from frozen. Vary the toppings to find your favourites.

400 g (14 oz) fresh pizza base from the chiller cabinet.
25 g (1 oz) pesto sauce
50 g (1¾ oz) passata or canned tomatoes, sieved

For the toppings
frozen broccoli florets, defrosted
1 courgette, sliced
mushrooms, sliced
a pinch of dried mixed herbs

1 Preheat the oven to Gas Mark 7/220°C/ 425°F.

2 Place the pizza base on a non-stick baking sheet and spread with the pesto and passata or sieved tomatoes.

3 Add the toppings and cook for 16–18 minutes.

Cook's tip

Fresh pizza bases from the chiller cabinet give a much better result than frozen ones, but be careful not to overcook them as they can become too dry and biscuit-like.

Fresh pizza bases can be frozen. Add your toppings later. To cook from frozen, add an extra 4 minutes

Variations

Instead of passata or sieved tomatoes use a thin scraping of tomato purée.

Suggestions for Point-free toppings include:

- sliced peppers
- sliced tomatoes
- sliced onions
- chillies (but beware!)

For these toppings you need to add the following Points to Total Points per recipe:

- 150 g (5½ oz) prawns, defrosted: 2½ Points/150 Calories
- 150 g (5½ oz) canned tuna in brine: 2 Points/160 Calories
- 150 g (5½ oz) cooked chicken tikka mini fillets: 3 Points/150 Calories
- 100 g (3½ oz) smoked wafer-thin turkey: 1½ Points/100 Calories
- 50 g (1¾ oz) grated half-fat Cheddar cheese: 3 Points/140 Calories
- 100 g (3½ oz) canned pineapple in natural juice ½ Point/35 Calories
- 6 olives: ½ Point/36 Calories
- 100 g (3½ oz) canned sweetcorn: 1½ Points/125 Calories

Squash Provençale

Ⓥ

0 Points per serving

0 Total Points per recipe

120 Calories per serving

4 Servings

Freezing recommended. Preparation and cooking time: 20 minutes.

Squash isn't commonly used, but it's cheap, comes in all sorts of shapes and sizes and with this recipe you can even freeze it. This is delicious with Springtime Lamb (page 94).

6 tomatoes, skinned and chopped
450 g (1 lb) squash, peeled and chopped into 2.5 cm (1-inch) cubes
2 onions, chopped
1 garlic clove, crushed (optional)
salt and freshly ground black pepper

1 Place the tomatoes and squash in a pan and cook over a gentle heat for about 10 minutes.

2 Add the onion and garlic, if using. Season. Cook until the onion is transparent but the squash still holds its shape (about 5 minutes).

3 Serve or freeze in rigid freezerproof boxes.

Variation

Use marrow or courgettes instead of the squash.

Fruity Pasta

V

3 Points per serving

6 Total Points per recipe

420 Calories per serving

2 Servings

Freezing not recommended. Preparation time: 15 minutes.

This recipe will help you to keep to the recommended 5 fruits or vegetables a day. You get 3 fruits and lots of vitamin C in just one serving. This dish may be heated, but is nice served chilled.

225 g (8 oz) canned pineapple rings in natural juice

1 red-skinned apple, cored

40 g (1½ oz) seedless grapes, halved

175 g (6 oz) cooked pasta bows

1 Chop the pineapple into pieces the same size as the cooked pasta. Put in a bowl.

2 Cut the apple into similarly sized pieces and mix with the pineapple.

3 Add the grapes and pasta and mix thoroughly ensuring the apple is covered with the juice so it doesn't turn brown.

4 Chill until ready to serve.

Cook's tip

Cook the pasta 'al dente' so that it retains a little bite. Other fruit may be added.

Variation

You can use any fruit you like – canned mandarin oranges make an excellent substitute for the pineapple.

Bean Napoletana

V

2 Points per serving

7 Total Points per recipe

120 Calories per serving

4 Servings

Freezing not recommended. Preparation and cooking time: 10 minutes.

What could be simpler than a dish based around a can of beans? This is packed with fibre and protein and takes only 10 minutes from start to finish. It's delicious with Pork aux Pommes (page 97).

420 g canned mixed beans, drained

420 g canned chopped tomatoes with herbs

1 garlic clove, crushed (optional)

1 Put the beans and tomatoes in a saucepan together with the garlic, if using. Bring to the boil and simmer uncovered to allow the sauce to reduce. When thickened, serve.

 Quorn and Rice Ratatouille

V

4 Points per serving

11½ Total Points per recipe

210 Calories per serving

4 Servings

Freezing not recommended. Preparation and cooking time: 25–30 minutes.

Quorn is so versatile and it's low in fat and Calories too. In this dish it absorbs the flavour of the ratatouille perfectly.

125 g (4½ oz) brown rice

low-fat cooking spray

1 onion, chopped

1 garlic clove, crushed

400 g (14 oz) canned ratatouille

225 g (8 oz) canned chopped tomatoes

1 teaspoon dried mixed herbs

125 g (4½ oz) Quorn, cubed

1 Cook the rice according to the packet instructions. Drain.

2 Spray a large saucepan with a little low-fat cooking spray. Cook the onion and garlic until the onion is transparent.

3 Stir in the ratatouille, tomatoes and herbs.

4 Add the Quorn and cook for 10 minutes. Season.

5 Stir in the rice and heat thoroughly.

Pear and Watercress Salad

Ⓥ

2 Points per serving

8 Total Points per recipe

135 Calories per serving

④ Servings

Freezing not recommended. Preparation time: 30 minutes + cooling + 15 minutes chilling.

A refreshing salad that is wonderful on a hot summer day. The brown rice gives it a crunchy, nutty taste. It's cooked exactly like white rice.

50 g (1¾ oz) long-grain brown rice
175 g (6 oz) plain cottage cheese
a pinch of cayenne pepper
410 g canned pears in natural juice,
*   drained and chopped*
2 bunches of watercress, trimmed
fat-free French dressing

Pear and Watercress Salad

1 Cook the rice in boiling salted water. Drain and leave to cool.

2 When the rice is cold mix the cheese, cayenne pepper and pears together and add to the rice.

3 Arrange the watercress in a ring on a flat dish and pile the rice mixture in the centre.

4 Chill for 15 minutes before serving with fat-free French dressing.

Cook's tip

To cool rice quickly, run cold water through it and drain well.

Variations

Peeled fresh pears could be used instead of canned. 1 pear is 1 Point or 60 Calories.

   Brown rice is best for this recipe, but other kinds are suitable.

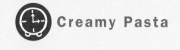

Creamy Pasta

Ⓥ

2½ Points per serving

11 Total Points per recipe

165 Calories per serving

④ Servings

Freezing not recommended. Preparation and cooking time: 10 minutes.

This recipe is ideal if you are in a hurry – it is quick, simple and filling.

350 g (12 oz) canned 99% fat-free
*   condensed mushroom soup*
350 g (12 oz) cooked pasta
400 g (14 oz) canned mixed vegetables,
*   drained*

1 Empty the soup into a saucepan and gently heat, do not boil.

2 Add cooked pasta and mixed vegetables. Serve hot.

Spanish Veggie Paella

V

3 Points per serving

11½ Total Points per recipe

250 Calories per serving

4 Servings

Freezing not recommended. Preparation: 10 minutes + 20 minutes cooking.

1 tablespoon oil, (preferably olive)

1 onion, sliced finely

1 teaspoon turmeric

175 g (6 oz) easy-cook long-grain rice

425 ml (¾ pint) hot vegetable stock,
either fresh or made with a cube

1 red pepper, de-seeded and cut into
fine strips

1 green pepper, de-seeded and cut into
fine strips

2 courgettes, sliced

400 g (14 oz) canned chopped tomatoes
with herbs

salt and freshly ground black pepper

1 Heat the oil in a non-stick pan, and gently stir-fry the onion till soft.

2 Add the turmeric and the rice and cook, stirring, for 1 minute.

3 Add the rest of the ingredients and bring to the boil.

4 Give the paella a good stir, and then lower the heat, cover and cook for 12–15 minutes until the rice is tender and all the liquid has been absorbed.

5 Adjust the seasoning and serve piping hot.

Egg and Potato Florentine

V

2½ Points per serving

9½ Total Points per recipe

195 Calories per serving

4 Servings

Freezing not recommended. Preparation time: 5 minutes + 15 minutes cooking. This can be prepared very quickly and easily with ingredients from the store-cupboard and freezer, and makes an ideal lunch or family supper dish.

450 g (1 lb) frozen spinach

400 g (14 oz) canned chopped tomatoes
with herbs

550 g can new potatoes, drained

4 medium eggs

salt and freshly ground black pepper

1 Preheat the oven to Gas Mark 6/200°C/400°F.

2 Cook the spinach according to the packet instructions for 2 or 3 minutes.

3 Drain the spinach well. Put the tomatoes, potatoes and spinach into an ovenproof dish, and season with salt and pepper.

4 Carefully break the eggs on top, and add a little more seasoning.

5 Bake for 10–15 minutes or until the eggs are set.

Weight Watchers tip

You can add a little low-fat cheese, but remember to add on the extra Points. 50 g (1¾ oz) half-fat Cheddar will add 35 Calories and 1 Point per serving.

Sweet and Sour Vegetables

V

1 Point per serving

1½ Total Points per recipe

165 Calories per serving

2 Servings

Freezing not recommended. Preparation time: 15 minutes.

This uses an interesting mix of vegetables, you can, of course, use different ones.

low-fat cooking spray

2 large carrots, cut into sticks

6 spring onions, trimmed and cut into
small pieces

100 g (3½ oz) baby sweetcorn, halved
lengthways

100 g (3½ oz) mangetout, trimmed

225 g (8 oz) canned pineapple pieces in
natural juice

1 teaspoon Chinese five spice

1 teaspoon cornflour

1 tablespoon light soy sauce

1 Heat a large pan or wok and spray with low-fat cooking spray. Stir-fry the carrots.

2 Add the spring onions, sweetcorn and mangetout.

3 Drain the pineapple pieces and reserve the juice. Add the pineapple pieces and the Chinese five spice.

4 Mix the cornflour to a cream with a little pineapple juice and add to the wok with the rest of the juice and the soy sauce.

Weight Watchers tip

Serve with wholemeal pitta bread, remembering to add the extra Points.

Leek and Pepper Tortilla

V

1½ Points per serving
6 Total Points per recipe
105 Calories per serving
4 Servings

Freezing not recommended. Preparation and cooking time: 10 minutes.
Eggs are always a handy standby and the leeks and pepper combine beautifully.

low-fat cooking spray
1 leek, cut into thin rings
1 red pepper, de-seeded and chopped
1 yellow pepper, de-seeded and chopped
4 eggs
salt and freshly ground black pepper

1 Spray a 20 cm (8-inch) omelette pan with a little low-fat cooking spray.
2 Preheat the grill.
3 Lightly fry the vegetables, turning constantly to avoid charring.
4 Lightly beat the eggs, season to taste and pour over the cooked vegetables.
5 Allow the heat to set the eggs. When nearly cooked pop the omelette under a hot grill to set the top.

Tagliatelle with Sage, Pimentos and Garlic

V

2½ Points per serving
9 Total Points per recipe
130 Calories per serving
4 Servings

Freezing not recommended. Preparation and cooking time: 20 minutes.
A superb combination of strong flavours.

1 onion, chopped
1 garlic clove, crushed
175 g (6 oz) canned pimentos, drained
1 teaspoon dried sage
350 g (12 oz) cooked green and white tagliatelle
125 g (4½ oz) low-fat plain fromage frais

1 Cook the onion and garlic in a little water.
2 Dice the pimentos and add to the onion with the dried sage.
3 Mix together with the tagliatelle and fromage frais and heat through.

Vegetable Kebabs with Tangy Sauce

V

2 Points per serving
7 Total Points per recipe
185 Calories per serving
4 Servings

Freezing not recommended. Preparation and cooking time: 30 minutes.
These are ideal for cooking on the barbecue.

a selection of fruit (e.g. 400 g canned apricots in natural juice, 400 g fresh pineapple – reserve any juice)
a selection of vegetables (e.g. courgettes, peppers, mushrooms, 250 g small new cooked potatoes, tomatoes)
low-fat cooking spray
225 g (8 oz) chopped tomatoes
1 onion, chopped
3 tablespoons white wine vinegar
1 tablespoon Worcestershire sauce
salt and freshly ground black pepper

1 Preheat the grill to medium.
2 Prepare all the fruit and vegetables by cutting them into equal-sized pieces. Thread them on kebab skewers and spray with low-fat cooking spray.
3 Grill the kebabs, turning them frequently so they don't burn.
4 Put the tomatoes in a saucepan. Add the onion and cook gently.
5 Add any juice from your selection of fruit, the vinegar and the Worcestershire sauce. Season to taste.
6 Serve the sauce poured over the kebabs.

Mushroom Stroganoff

Cook's tip

Flat metal kebab skewers are best – they make it easier to turn the kebabs. If you are using wooden skewers soak them in water for ½ hour before you use them to stop them burning.

Weight Watchers tip

You can really go to town with masses of colourful vegetables, but at the same time you're being really economical with your Points.

Ⓥ

1½ Points per serving

6½ Total Points per recipe

90 Calories per serving

❹ Servings

Freezing not recommended. Preparation and cooking time: 10 minutes.
Be adventurous and try a mix of different sorts of mushroom. Serve with plain boiled rice or pasta, adding the extra Points.

225 g (8 oz) mixed mushrooms (e.g. shiitake, chestnut, closed-cup), sliced

2 teaspoons oil
2 dessertspoons lemon juice
175 g (6 oz) low-fat soft cheese
chopped fresh herbs, to garnish
salt and freshly ground black pepper

1 In a large pan lightly cook the sliced mushrooms in the oil and the lemon juice. Do not overcook.
2 Add the soft cheese, season and mix together until the mushrooms are coated.
3 Serve sprinkled with chopped herbs.

Mushroom Stroganoff

Jacket Potatoes with Pepperslaw

 ## Peanut Peppers

 ## Quick Mediterranean Vegetable Risotto

Ⓥ

3½ Points per serving

315 Calories per serving

❶ Serving

Freezing not recommended. Preparation time: 10 minutes or an hour according to method used to cook potato.
A very colourful and tasty salad.

150 g (5½ oz) potato, scrubbed
½ red pepper, de-seeded and sliced thinly
½ green pepper, de-seeded and sliced thinly
½ yellow pepper, de-seeded and sliced thinly
2 tablespoons Weight Watchers from Heinz low-fat dressing
25 g (1 oz) black seedless grapes, halved
15 g (½ oz) pine nuts

1 If you're cooking your potato in the microwave, prick the potato with a fork at least 4 times and cook for 4–6 minutes depending on the microwave output. If you're cooking more than 1 potato adjust cooking time accordingly, e.g. 2 potatoes will take 10 minutes. To cook the potato in a conventional oven preheat the oven to Gas Mark 6/200°C/400°F. Put the potato on a potato spike or metal skewer, or prick it and place directly on the oven shelf. Cook for 1–1¼ hours until it is soft to touch.
2 Mix the peppers together in the dressing.
3 Add the grapes. Stuff the potato with this filling and sprinkle pine nuts on the top.

Ⓥ

3½ Points per serving

14 Total Points per recipe

260 Calories per serving

❹ Servings

Freezing not recommended. Preparation time: 30 minutes + 30 minutes cooking.
A colourful meal with a hint of crunch.

175 g (6 oz) long-grain rice
1 onion, chopped
500 ml (18 fl oz) vegetable stock
4 green peppers
50 g (1¾ oz) peanuts
salt and freshly ground black pepper

1 Cook the rice and onion in the stock.
2 Preheat the oven to Gas Mark 6/200°C/400°F.
3 Slice the tops off the peppers and remove the seeds.
4 When the rice is cooked and the water all absorbed, mix in the peanuts. Season to taste.
5 Fill the peppers with this mixture, replace the tops and wrap each one in foil.
6 Cook in oven for 20–30 minutes until the peppers are soft.

Cook's tip

These are great to cook on the barbecue, but allow a little longer cooking time.

Variation

Add some garlic and a little chilli to the filling before you add the peanuts.

Ⓥ

4 Points per serving

8½ Total Points per recipe

255 Calories per serving

❷ Servings

Freezing not recommended. Preparation and cooking time: 10 minutes.
This can be made with easy-cook, frozen or canned rice. I've used canned here because a can is just right for two servings. Canned rice is the kind of standby that it's always handy to have in the store-cupboard.

277 g can Uncle Ben's Express Rice
390 g can Tesco's Ratatouille Provençal
1 teaspoon dried Herbes de Provence
salt and freshly ground black pepper

1 Cook the rice according to the instructions for 3 minutes.
2 Mix in the ratatouille and simmer gently for a further 2 minutes.
3 Add the herbs and seasoning and serve piping hot.

Variation

Throw in a few halved button mushrooms and, if you like, some prawns. Remember to alter the Points.

Crunchy Rice Salad **Page 113**
Jacket Potatoes with Pepperslaw

Leek, Tomato and Cheese Italienne

V

2½ Points per serving

10½ Total Points per recipe

205 Calories per serving

4 Servings

Freezing: not recommended. Preparation and cooking time: 20 minutes.

This is another handy, cheap, midweek dish. It can be made with frozen leeks if you happen to have them in the freezer.

2 leeks, chopped, boiled and drained, or 450 g (1 lb) frozen, ready-chopped leeks

550 g can new potatoes, drained and halved

300 g jar Heinz Tomato Frito, (see tip)

1 teaspoon Schwartz Italian seasoning or Herbes de Provence

100 g (3½ oz) low-fat mozzarella cheese, sliced thinly (see tip)

salt and freshly ground black pepper

1 Preheat the grill.

2 Put the cooked leeks, potatoes and Tomato Frito in a shallow, flameproof dish and heat thoroughly.

3 Stir in the Italian seasoning or herbs, some salt and pepper, and top with the cheese.

4 Put under a hot grill until cheese is bubbling. Serve immediately.

Cook's tips

You can, if you like, use fresh boiled potatoes, but the dish will take longer to prepare, and they are liable to break up when combined with the other ingredients.

If you can't get Tomato Frito, use the same quantity of passata (sieved tomatoes) with onion and garlic. Calories and Points will be the same.

Low-fat mozzarella cheese is widely available. Sainsbury's have it under their own brand label, and it is also made by the Italian cheesemakers Galbani. If you can't find it, substitute low-fat Edam.

Quick, Quick Mushroom Risotto

V

3½ Points per serving

7 Total Points per recipe

230 Calories per serving

2 Servings

Freezing not recommended. Preparation and cooking time: 15 minutes.

This is ideal for a simple, in-front-of-the-telly supper. It's low-budget, super-quick and super-tasty!

277 g can Uncle Ben's Express rice

½ × 295 g can 99% fat-free condensed mushroom soup

100 g (3½ oz) frozen mixed peas and sweetcorn, cooked and drained

100 g (3½ oz) button mushrooms, sliced

1 teaspoon Schwartz Italian seasoning or Herbes de Provence

salt and freshly ground black pepper

1 Cook the rice for 3 minutes, according to the instructions.

2 Stir in the mushroom soup, peas and sweetcorn and mushrooms.

3 Reheat and season to taste with the Italian seasoning or herbs and some salt and pepper. Serve piping hot.

Cook's tip

The rest of the soup makes a good quick snack when you're on your own!

Variation

Non-vegetarians can add cooked chicken or prawns. Remember to add the Points.

Chick-pea and Beany Mexican Hot-Pot

Ⓥ

5½ Points per serving

22 Total Points per recipe

335 Calories per serving

4 Servings

Freezing recommended. Preparation and cooking time: 15 minutes.

This is very tasty, very filling and just right for a chilly winter's night.

1 teaspoon vegetable oil
1 onion, sliced finely
420 g can chick-peas, drained
420 g can kidney beans in chilli sauce
400 g (14 oz) canned chopped tomatoes
    with garlic
salt and freshly ground black pepper
4 medium soft flour tortillas, to serve
    (see tip)

1 Preheat the grill.

2 Heat the oil in a non-stick pan and gently fry the onion until soft, but not browned.

3 Add the chick-peas, the kidney beans with their sauce and the tomatoes. Mix well and heat through gently.

4 Grill the tortillas for a few seconds on each side to warm them.

3 Season the bean mixture to taste and serve with the warmed tortillas.

Cook's tip

Tortillas are widely available from supermarkets, plain or with garlic and coriander. A medium pitta bread makes a good substitute; add ½ Point or 15 Calories per serving.

Moroccan Chick-pea and Apricot Pilaff

Ⓥ

8½ Points per serving

17 Total Points per recipe

450 Calories per serving

2 Servings

Freezing not recommended. Preparation and cooking time: 10 minutes.

Another super-quick dish, this time with a Moroccan theme. All the ingredients come straight from the store-cupboard.

410 g can apricot halves in fruit juice
277 g can Uncle Ben's Express rice
420 g can chick-peas, drained
2 tablespoons raisins
salt and freshly ground black pepper

1 Chop the apricots roughly and put them, with their juice, in a non-stick pan.

2 Add the rice, stir and bring to the boil.

3 Lower the heat, cover tightly and cook for 3 minutes or until rice is tender.

4 Add the chick-peas and raisins, stir through and reheat gently, then season to taste before serving.

Cook's tip

Garnish with diced red or green peppers and some flaked almonds. Don't forget to add the extra Points for the almonds.

Cheesy Egg and Potato Pie

Ⓥ

5½ Points per serving

22½ Total Points per recipe

235 Calories per serving

4 Servings

Freezing not recommended. Preparation and cooking time: 25 minutes + 20 minutes baking.

Here's another low-budget winter-warmer. The recipe originated from Tony Blair's old school, where it was made with a basic thick white sauce. This version is tastier – and healthier!

450 g (1 lb) potatoes, cooked, mashed
    and seasoned
4 medium eggs, hard-boiled and halved
295 g can 99% fat-free condensed
    mushroom soup
50 g (1¾ oz) Shape Mature Cheddar
    cheese, grated
25 g (1 oz) fresh wholemeal breadcrumbs
salt and freshly ground black pepper

1 Preheat the oven to Gas Mark 6/200°C/ 400°F.

2 Put the mashed potatoes into an ovenproof serving dish, and top with the eggs, cut-side down.

3 Spoon on the soup and season with salt and black pepper.

4 Mix the cheese with the breadcrumbs, sprinkle on top and bake for 20 minutes or until crisp and browned. Serve immediately.

There's really no end to the variety of fish and you'll find that the fish featured in this chapter are widely available in supermarkets. They don't need any special preparation and, since fish tends to cook quite quickly, these are by definition quick meals.

We've included some favourite family dishes, such as Tuna and Sweetcorn Jacket Potato and Salmon Fish Cakes. But if you really enjoy the taste of good fish then you might want to be a little more adventurous and conjure up Eastern Salmon, Pesto Haddock with Crispy Crust, Mediterranean Mackerel or Prawn Puri.

fish

Cod in Parsley Sauce

2 Points per serving
8 Total Points per recipe
165 Calories per serving
4 Servings

Freezing recommended. Preparation and cooking time: 20 minutes.

This recipe uses a sauce mix from a packet so there's no need to worry about lumpy sauces. Choose a mix that uses milk rather than water – that way you can use skimmed milk to keep the Points low.

4 frozen fish fillets, defrosted if
  necessary
1 onion, chopped finely
1 bay leaf
20 g packet Colman's Parsley Sauce Mix
275 ml (9½ fl oz) skimmed milk
salt and freshly ground black pepper
lemon wedges, to garnish

1 Put the fish, onion and bay leaf in a frying pan or shallow saucepan. Add just enough water to cover and poach the fish until it's just cooked. Reserve the cooking liquid.
2 Use the skimmed milk and the cooking liquid to make up the sauce according to the instructions on the packet. Season to taste
3 Serve the fish on hot plates, smothered in parsley sauce and garnished with lemon wedges.

 ## Sizzling Fish Steaks with Tomato Sauce

3½ Points per serving
11 Total Points per recipe
260 Calories per serving
3 Servings

Freezing recommended. Preparation and cooking time: 30 minutes.

Simple store-cupboard ingredients – frozen breadcrumbed fish steaks and a can of chopped tomatoes with garlic and herbs – combine to make a delicious fish supper. Choose a pan that you're happy to take straight to the table, so everyone's taste-buds are awakened with the sizzling sounds.

3 frozen cod steaks in breadcrumbs
1 teaspoon oil
½ teaspoon dill pepper
lemon juice
For the sauce
1 teaspoon oil
1 small onion, chopped finely
400 g (14 oz) canned chopped tomatoes
  with garlic and herbs

1 Grill the fish as instructed on the packet.
2 Meanwhile, prepare the sauce. Heat the oil and fry the onion for a few minutes.
3 Add the tomatoes and simmer until they become soft and mushy. Add a little water if you prefer a thinner sauce.
4 Heat a non-stick frying pan and pour in the oil. Put the cooked fish in the pan and sprinkle over the dill pepper.
5 Heat the fish until it sizzles. Just before serving, drizzle the lemon juice into the pan. Serve from the pan, with the tomato sauce.

Tuna Sauce

1½ Points per serving
6½ Total Points per recipe
160 Calories per serving
4 Servings

Freezing not recommended. Preparation and cooking time: 25 minutes.

This versatile sauce can be served with pasta, rice, jacket potatoes or simply added to vegetable dishes to provide a little extra protein!

1 onion, chopped finely
1 tablespoon vegetable oil
1 green pepper, de-seeded and sliced
½ teaspoon paprika or 1–2 fresh green
  chillies, de-seeded and chopped finely
2 garlic cloves, crushed
400 g (14 oz) canned tomatoes
400 g (14 oz) canned tuna in brine,
  drained
salt and freshly ground black pepper

1 Cook the onion in the oil for about 5 minutes over a medium heat.
2 Add the pepper, paprika or chillies and the garlic. Cook over a low heat for a further 2–3 minutes, stirring continuously.
3 Add the canned tomatoes and the tuna. Continue to cook over a low heat for about 10 minutes, stirring occasionally. Add a little water if the sauce becomes too dry. Season with a little salt and pepper.

Variation
Canned crabmeat can be used instead of the tuna. The Points remain the same. Calories per serving will be 130.

Mediterranean Fish Parcels

2 Points per serving

4 Total Points per recipe

200 Calories per serving

2 Servings

Freezing not recommended. Preparation time: 10 minutes + 20 minutes cooking. The aroma of garlic and basil, the bright red and green of peppers and tomatoes, the flavours of olive oil and lime – this dish really conjures up the Mediterranean. Serve straight from the oven as all the flavours are sealed in individual pockets.

low-fat cooking spray

2 × 175 g (6 oz) frozen white fish steaks or fillets, defrosted if necessary

½ teaspoon crushed garlic

½ teaspoon dried basil

¼ teaspoon Herbes de Provence

¼ red pepper, sliced

¼ green pepper, sliced

6 cherry tomatoes, halved

2 teaspoons olive oil

1 Preheat the oven to Gas Mark 4/180°C/ 350°F. Take 2 squares of foil, each big enough to take 1 fish steak or fillet. Spray each square with 3 sprays of low-fat cooking spray. Put a fish steak or fillet on each foil square.

2 Top with the garlic and herbs.

3 Add the peppers and tomatoes. Drizzle a teaspoon of olive oil over each piece of fish.

4 Make the foil into parcels and bake for 15 minutes.

5 Open up the foil, spoon the juices over the fish and return to the oven for about 5 minutes – you may need less cooking time if the fish is flat and thin. Check that the fish is fully cooked before serving.

Mediterranean Fish Parcels

 Fish Kedgeree

3 Points per serving

11 Total Points per recipe

190 Calories per serving

4 Servings

Freezing recommended. Preparation and cooking time: 45 minutes.
This family favourite can be prepared in advance. It's a combination of lots of healthy ingredients all in one pot.

75 g (2¾ oz) rice
200 ml (7 fl oz) vegetable stock made
    with a stock cube
300 g (10½ oz) smoked haddock
1 tablespoon vegetable oil
100 g (3½ oz) mushrooms, sliced
100 g (3½ oz) onions, sliced
100 g (3½ oz) cooked peas
2 teaspoons lemon juice

a pinch of cayenne pepper
salt and freshly ground black pepper

1 Preheat the oven to Gas Mark 3/170°C/ 320°F.
2 Cook the rice in the vegetable stock.
3 Place the fish in a shallow pan and cover with water. Bring to the boil and simmer for 10–15 minutes until cooked.
4 Drain and flake the fish. Remove any bones.
5 Heat the oil and sauté the mushrooms and onions for about 5 minutes over a medium heat.
6 Mix the cooked fish, rice, peas, mushrooms and onions together. Add the remaining ingredients and place the mixture in an ovenproof dish. Cover with a lid or some foil.
7 Bake for 15–20 minutes. Serve hot.

Weight Watchers tip
Fish is an excellent source of protein and it's also low in fat.

Variation
Smoked cod or smoked coley can be used instead of haddock.

Fish Kedgeree

Baked Fish with Crunchy Onions

3 Points per serving

305 Calories per serving

1 Serving

Freezing not recommended. Preparation and cooking time: 45 minutes.

125 g (4½ oz) haddock fillets, defrosted
*   if frozen*
1 large onion, sliced
100 g (3½ oz) mushrooms, sliced
200 ml semi-skimmed milk to cover fish
1 tablespoon cornflour
salt and freshly ground black pepper

1 Preheat the oven to Gas Mark 6/200°C/400°F. Place the fish, onions and mushrooms in an ovenproof dish.
2 Pour enough milk over the fish to completely cover it. Cover with a lid or some foil.
3 Bake for about 40 minutes.
4 Take the fish out of the cooking liquid and set aside. Pour the cooking liquid into a pan. Make a paste by mixing the cornflour with a little cold water. Mix the paste into the liquid and heat till the mixture boils and thickens.
5 Pour this sauce over the fish. Season with a little salt and pepper. Serve hot.

Variation
Any firm-fleshed white fish can be used for this dish.

 ### Baked Cod with Tomatoes

3 Points per serving

11½ Total Points per recipe

170 Calories per serving

4 Servings

Freezing not recommended. Preparation and cooking time: 25 minutes.
There is an impressive range of fresh fish available at reasonable prices at our supermarkets nowadays. This dish, like most fish recipes, is quick and easy to prepare.

1 tablespoon vegetable oil
1 garlic clove, chopped finely
25 g (1 oz) fresh white breadcrumbs
4 × 150 g (5½ oz) fresh cod steaks
400 g (14 oz) canned plum tomatoes,
*   drained*
salt and freshly ground black pepper

1 Preheat the oven to Gas Mark 6/200°C/400°F.
2 Heat the oil in a non-stick pan and sauté the garlic for a few seconds.
3 Stir in the breadcrumbs and cook until they turn golden brown.
4 Put the fish in a roasting tin and pile on the tomatoes and the breadcrumbs. Season to taste.
5 Bake for 15 minutes or until the fish is cooked.

Oodles of Noodles with Prawns

6 Points per serving

24 Total Points per recipe

520 Calories per serving

4 Servings

Freezing not recommended. Preparation and cooking time: 25 minutes.
A dry curry-like dish with sweet and sour flavours.

350 g (12 oz) Chinese noodles
2 tablespoons vegetable oil
200 g (7 oz) frozen raw tiger prawns,
*   thawed and drained*
2 garlic cloves, chopped finely
3 tablespoons sun-dried tomato paste
200 g (7 oz) cherry tomatoes
salt and freshly ground black pepper

1 Cook the noodles in a large saucepan of boiling water following the instructions on the packet.
2 Heat the oil in a large frying pan. Add the prawns and the garlic. Stir-fry over a medium heat for 3–5 minutes.
3 Stir in the tomato paste and mix well. Add 2 tablespoons water and the cherry tomatoes and mix well.
4 Toss the prawn and tomato mixture into the drained noodles. Season to taste and serve immediately.

Variation
Instead of prawns you can use 250 g (9 oz) lean pork, sliced into strips. Add ½ Point or 55 Calories per serving.

Mackerel with Mustard

7½ Points per serving

29 Total Points per recipe

405 Calories per serving

4 Servings

Freezing not recommended. Preparation and cooking time: 15 minutes.

4 mackerel fillets, each weighing around 175 g (6 oz)

1 tablespoon lemon juice

2 teaspoons made mustard

salt and freshly ground black pepper

100 g (3½ oz) green grapes, seeded and halved, to garnish

1 lemon, cut into wedges, to serve

1 Preheat the grill to medium. Line the grill pan with foil and put the fish in the pan.

2 Pour the lemon juice over the fish and spread the mustard on top.

3 Season and grill for 10–15 minutes, turning once.

4 Garnish the top of each fish with the grapes and serve with lemon wedges.

Fisherman's Pie

3½ Points per serving

14 Total Points per recipe

270 Calories per serving

4 Servings

Freezing not recommended. Preparation time: 30 minutes + 1 hour cooking.

A tasty fish dish with potato topping that only needs a green vegetable to go with it. Try Roasted Broccoli (page 69),and cook them both together in the oven.

400 g (14 oz) smoked haddock fillets, skinned

100 g (3½ oz) fresh or frozen prawns (defrost frozen prawns thoroughly in fridge)

1 onion, chopped finely

salt and freshly ground black pepper

For the sauce

15 g (½ oz) low-fat spread

1 dessertspoon cornflour

200 ml (7 fl oz) skimmed milk

¼ – ½ teaspoon cayenne

For the topping

450 g (1 lb) potatoes, peeled and boiled

100 ml (3½ fl oz) skimmed milk

1 Preheat the oven to Gas Mark 3/170°C/350°F.

2 Place the smoked haddock in a shallow ovenproof casserole. Add the prawns and onion. Season.

3 Melt the reduced-fat spread in a saucepan.

4 Add the cornflour and mix.

5 Add the skimmed milk and stir over the heat until thickened.

6 Add the cayenne and cook for 2 minutes.

7 Add the sauce to the fish in the casserole dish. Do not worry if there seems to be very little sauce – the fish releases more liquid as it cooks.

8 Mash the boiled potatoes and skimmed milk together. Season.

9 Top the fish mixture with the mashed potato, making sure it is all covered.

10 Bake for 1 hour.

Cook's tip

You don't need to add salt to this dish, as the smoked fish is already salty. Choose chunky fillets of fish, rather than the tail end for this recipe.

Weight Watchers tip

If serving with Roasted Broccoli the Points will remain the same.

Variations

Smoked cod or any white fish could be used instead of smoked haddock.

If you like add some chopped fresh parsley to the sauce or the topping or both!

Tuna and Sweetcorn Jacket Potato

3½ Points per serving

15 Total Points per recipe

330 Calories per serving

4 Servings

Freezing not recommended. Preparation time: 10 minutes + 1 hour cooking.

This recipe beats takeaway versions by a mile. The flesh of the cooked potato is mixed with the flavoursome filling and the whole thing is grilled to give a crunchy topping. Serve with sliced tomatoes.

There are so many delicious fillings for jacket potatoes, just glance at the variations for some interesting alternatives to this one.

4 medium-sized baking potatoes (about 175 g/6 oz each)

For the filling

2 × 185 g can tuna in brine, drained

325 g (11½ oz) canned sweetcorn in water, drained

4 dessertspoons tomato relish or pickle

1 Preheat the oven to Gas Mark 8/230°C/ 450°F.

2 Wash and dry the potatoes and pierce them with a skewer.

3 Place on the middle shelf of the oven (you don't need a baking tray). Bake for 1 hour.

4 Check that the potatoes are soft and take them out of the oven.

5 Put the tuna, sweetcorn and pickle in a large bowl.

6 Slice the potatoes in half and scoop out the flesh, adding it to the bowl. Mash the mixture together well.

7 Put the potato skins in a shallow ovenproof dish which will support them. Fill them with the potato mixture.

8 Place under a hot grill for 2 minutes.

Cooks' tip

Jacket potatoes can be microwaved to save time. Wrap each potato in a sheet of kitchen paper and cook on full power for about 6 minutes (or until the potato is soft). Allow the potatoes to stand for 1 minute.

Variations

Try these other fillings. All the quantities are for four people and the Points and Calories include the potatoes.

•   250 g (9 oz) reduced-Calorie coleslaw + 1 chopped apple + 15 g (½ oz) currants. Simply pile on top of the potato. This is 3½ Points/220 Calories per serving.

•   100 g (3½ oz) half-fat Cheddar cheese + 4 dessertspoons tomato relish. Either mash with potato and grill or spread over the top and let it melt! This is 3½ Points/230 Calories per serving.

Prawn Puri

4½ Points per serving

18½ Total Points per recipe

230 Calories per serving

4 Servings

Freezing not recommended. Preparation and cooking time: 20 minutes.

Garlic and coriander naans are particularly good for this recipe.

low-fat cooking spray

1 onion, sliced

1 green pepper, de-seeded and cut into 2 cm (¾-inch) strips

3 dessertspoons tomato pickle or fruit chutney

225 g (8 oz) fresh or frozen prawns (defrost frozen prawns thoroughly)

1 teaspoon curry powder

4 mini-naan breads (about 60 g each)

1 Spray a large non-stick saucepan with 4 sprays of low-fat cooking spray. Add the onion and green pepper and cook until soft.

2 Preheat the grill to hot.

3 Add the tomato pickle and 1 tablespoon water to the pan.

4 Add the prawns and curry powder and mix well.

5 Warm the naan bread under a hot grill and serve with the prawn mixture piled in the middle.

Weight Watchers tip

Serve with plain yogurt and cucumber and sprinkle with chopped fresh parsley or coriander leaves. Add the extra Points for the yogurt.

Savoury Prawn Rice

2½ Points per serving
10 Total Points per recipe
190 Calories per serving
❹ Servings

Freezing not recommended. Preparation and cooking time: 30 minutes.
A one-pot meal for when you're in a hurry. Serve with soy sauce and a green salad.

1 packet Curry-flavour Savoury Rice
15 g (½ oz) currants
100 g (3½ oz) spring onions, sliced thinly
100 g (3½ oz) carrot, grated
225 g (8 oz) prawns, fresh or defrosted

1 Put the rice mixture and currants in a saucepan and add the quantity of water stated on the packet.
2 Bring to the boil and simmer for 20 minutes until the water is absorbed.
3 Add the spring onions, grated carrots and prawns and cook for a further 2 minutes, stirring gently so the rice doesn't become too mushy.

Cook's tip
Make sure frozen prawns are defrosted thoroughly in the fridge and drained before use.

Variations
Use different flavours of savoury rice or add other vegetables like green peas or tinned sweetcorn (remember to add the Points). Omit the prawns for a vegetarian option (Points will be 1½ per serving and Calories will be 130 per serving).

 ## Salmon Cakes Pizzaolo

4½ Points per serving
18 Total Points per recipe
240 Calories per serving
❹ Servings

Freezing recommended after step 4. Preparation time: 40 minutes + 20 minutes chilling + 40 minutes cooking. These salmon cakes have a definite Italian flavour.

450 g (1 lb) potatoes, boiled
200 ml (7 fl oz) skimmed milk
300 g (10½ oz) canned pink salmon in brine, skin and bones removed
4 spring onions, chopped very finely
100 g (3½ oz) dried breadcrumbs
salt and freshly ground pepper
1 tub (150 g/5½ oz) chunky salsa dip (Tesco's is good!), to serve

1 In a large mixing bowl, mash together the potatoes and half the skimmed milk.
2 Add the salmon, spring onions, salt and pepper and mix together. Your hands are good for this!
3 Divide the mixture into four and shape each to form a cake shape about 1 cm (½ inch) deep.
4 Dip each salmon cake into the remainder of the skimmed milk. Then roll each one in breadcrumbs on all sides.
5 Chill in the fridge for 20 minutes (if you're in a hurry you can miss this out).
6 Preheat the oven to Gas Mark 8/230°C/450°F.
7 Place on a non-stick baking tray and place on the middle shelf of the oven for 40 minutes turning once.
8 Serve with salsa dip.

Cook's tip
You could also make 8 smaller salmon cakes to serve as a starter (2 Points each), with crispy shredded lettuce or Chinese leaves.

Variation
These cakes are also good made with canned tuna in brine or any cooked white fish. The Points will be 3½ per serving. Calories will be 205 per serving.

Salmon Cakes Pizzaola

Salmon and Mushrooms

3½ Points per serving
7½ Total Points per recipe
220 Calories per serving
2 Servings

Freezing not recommended. Preparation and cooking time: 5–15 minutes.
Salmon is often cheaper than white fish and is always easily available. This recipe is simple enough for a quick supper, and special enough for entertaining.

2 medium salmon steaks or fillets
*   (100 g/3½ oz each)*
300 g (10½ oz) can 99% fat-free
*   condensed mushroom soup*
4 button mushrooms, sliced
salt and freshly ground black pepper
1 lemon, cut into wedges to garnish

1 Preheat the oven to Gas Mark 5/190°C/ 375°F. Wrap each piece of salmon in foil and bake in the oven for 10 minutes. Alternatively wrap the fish in baking parchment and cook in the microwave for 4 minutes.
2 Empty the soup into a saucepan and add the sliced mushrooms. Heat gently. Season to taste.
3 Pour the sauce over the cooked salmon and serve garnished with lemon.

Tuna and Gnocchi Bake

3½ Points per serving
14½ Total Points per recipe
290 Calories per serving
4 Servings

Freezing see tip. Preparation time: 20 minutes + 30 minutes cooking.
Potato gnocchi are little Italian potato dumplings. They make an interesting base for this dish. They are normally found in the chiller cabinet.

400 g (14 oz) packet potato gnocchi
300 g (10½ oz) canned tuna in brine
300 ml (½ pint) skimmed milk
1 packet Colman's Savoury White
*   Sauce Mix*
2 teaspoons tomato purée
¼ teaspoon chilli powder
2 tomatoes, sliced thinly
salt

1 Preheat the oven to Gas Mark 5/190°C/ 375°F.
2 Simmer the potato gnocchi in lightly salted water for 3 minutes and then drain.
3 Place the gnocchi in an ovenproof casserole and cover with chunks of tuna.
4 Use the skimmed milk to make up the sauce mix as directed on the packet.
5 Add the tomato purée and chilli powder and stir well.
6 Pour the sauce over the tuna and potato gnocchi and top with the sliced tomatoes.
7 Bake in the oven for ½ hour.

Cook's tip
This goes well with French Beans with Almonds (page 69), but remember to add the Points.

You can freeze this bake after step 6, but make sure you defrost it before cooking and add an extra 10 minutes to the baking time.

Variation
Top with savoury breadcrumbs or crushed cornflakes, adding the extra Points.

Oriental Huss

4 Points per serving
16½ Total Points per recipe
190 Calories per serving
4 Servings

Freezing not recommended. Preparation and cooking time: 15 minutes.
An inexpensive and simple dish for friends or family. Serve with rice.

low-fat cooking spray
100 g (3¾ oz) mushrooms, sliced
2 tablespoons lemon juice
1 jar 'light' Sweet and Sour Sauce
450 g (1 lb) huss, cubed (see tip)
salt and freshly ground black pepper

1 Spray a little low-fat cooking spray into a large saucepan. Add the mushrooms and lemon juice and lightly cook.
2 Add the sauce and heat through. Season to taste.
3 Add fish and cook gently for 5 minutes.

Cook's tips

Huss is also known as dog fish or rock salmon. It's generally a cheap fish. Ask the fishmonger to remove the bone for you.

For a special meal use monkfish and a few prawns but check your Points!

 ## Eastern Salmon

3½ Points per serving
14½ Total Points per recipe
230 Calories per serving
4 Servings

Freezing not recommended. Preparation time: 5 minutes + 20 minutes cooking.
Salmon is now readily available and very reasonably priced. Try it this way, cooked with spices. Served with green vegetables and Tomato Rice (page 116). A wonderful meal to impress guests with – and only 5 minutes to prepare.

3 dessertspoons soy sauce
1 teaspoon clear honey
½ teaspoon Chinese five spice powder
4 × 125 g (4½ oz) fresh or frozen salmon fillets

1 Preheat the oven to Gas Mark 6/200°C/ 400°F.
2 Mix together the soy sauce, honey and Chinese five spice powder in a shallow ovenproof dish.
3 Roll the salmon in the mixture so all the sides are coated. Place skin-side down in the dish.
4 Bake in the oven for 20 minutes until the fish is cooked.

Cook's tip

Don't worry that there isn't enough sauce – this quantity is plenty to cover four pieces of fish lightly.

Weight Watchers tip

If serving with Tomato Rice (page 116) add 2 Points per portion.

Variations

I prefer salmon fillets, which have no bones, but steaks would be fine. You could also use trout or cod. The Points per serving will be 2 with trout and 1½ with cod. The Calories per serving will be 160 with trout and 105 with cod.

Cod Portuguese

1 Point per serving

4½ Total Points per recipe

100 Calories per serving

4 Servings

Freezing recommended. Preparation time: 15 minutes + 25 minutes cooking. This has all the authentic flavours of sunny Portugal. To serve it in traditional Portuguese fashion, make sure you have some boiled potatoes on the side! Remember to add the Points.

400 g (14 oz) canned chopped tomatoes with onions and peppers

4 × 92 g skinless, boneless frozen cod steaks

½ teaspoon garlic powder

8 black olives

salt and freshly ground black pepper

chopped fresh parsley or coriander, to garnish (optional)

1 Preheat the oven to Gas Mark 6/200°C/400°F.

2 Put the tomatoes in an ovenproof dish.

3 Add the fish steaks and season with salt, pepper and the garlic powder.

4 Bake for 20 minutes. Arrange the olives on top and bake for a further 5 minutes or until fish is cooked through.

5 Garnish with parsley or coriander, if using, before serving.

Cook's tip

Cook the potatoes while the fish is in the oven.

Variation

Use haddock steaks instead of cod. Points and Calories will be the same.

Cod Portuguese

Mediterranean Mackerel

7½ Points per serving

30½ Total Points per recipe

450 Calories per serving

4 Servings

Freezing not recommended. Preparation and cooking time: 30 minutes.
This is an excellent way to serve this low-price fish.

250 g (9 oz) potatoes, peeled and sliced thinly
low-fat cooking spray
4 × 175 g (6 oz) mackerel fillets
1 tomato, sliced
4 black olives, halved (optional)
1 lime, cut into wedges
salt and freshly ground black pepper

1 Preheat the oven Gas Mark 5/190°C/375°F.
2 Parboil the potato slices for 5 minutes.
3 Lightly spray an ovenproof dish with low-fat cooking spray and spread the potatoes in an even layer over the bottom of the dish.
4 Lay the mackerel fillets on top, season and cover the dish with foil.
5 Bake in oven for about 15 minutes, but the exact timing will depend on the size of the mackerel fillets.
6 Remove the foil and garnish with tomato, olives and lime.

Weight Watchers tip

Oily fish can be high in fat, but remember that fish oils are good for you, so try to include fish in family meals.

Crab Chowder

7 Points per serving

27 Total Points per recipe

250 Calories per serving

4 Servings

Freezing recommended for up to 1 month. Preparation and cooking time: 15 minutes.
Try this for a warming filling soup. You won't need much more after this! Serve with crusty wholemeal bread (remember to add the extra Points).

1 large potato, peeled and diced finely
600 ml (1 pint) fish stock made with a cube
450 g (1 lb) brown crab meat
350 g (12 oz) canned creamed sweetcorn
salt and freshly ground black pepper

1 Cook the diced potato in the fish stock until soft – about 5 minutes.
2 Add the crab meat and sweetcorn, cover and simmer until thoroughly hot. Season to taste and serve at once.

Cook's tip

Fish counters often have frozen crab meat. The brown meat is cheaper than the white.

 Cod St Clements

2½ Points per serving

10½ Total Points per recipe

170 Calories per serving

4 Servings

Freezing not recommended. Preparation time: 10 minutes.
A marvellously quick and simple dish in which two flavours combine to bring out the best in each other. Serve with broccoli and new potatoes.

400 g (14 oz) can grapefruit segments in natural juice
4 × 175 g (6 oz) fresh or frozen cod steaks

1 Take a shallow pan with a lid and heat the grapefruit in it.
2 Put the fish on top of the grapefruit and put the lid on.
3 Gently cook until the fish turns white – this will take 3–5 minutes for fresh fish (depending on the thickness of the fish) and another 2 minutes if the fish is being cooked from frozen.

Cook's tip

Do not overcook the fish or it will fall apart.

 **Pesce Italiano**

5 Points per serving

10½ Total Points per recipe

300 Calories per serving

2 Servings

Freezing not recommended. Preparation time: 15 minutes.

One of my favourites, simple, tasty and filling! Serve with a crisp green salad.

225 g (8 oz) white fish, cubed

2 tablespoons dry white wine

50 g (1¾ oz) mushrooms, sliced

1 courgette, sliced thinly

125 g (4½ oz) multi-coloured pasta shells, cooked

175 g (6 oz) low-fat soft cheese

salt and freshly ground black pepper

1 Poach the fish in the white wine for about 5 minutes.

2 Add the mushrooms and courgette.

3 Mix with pasta and low-fat soft cheese. Season to taste and serve at once.

 Salmon Fish Cakes

9 Points per serving

18 Total Points per recipe

440 Calories per serving

2 Servings

Freezing recommended. Preparation time: 30 minutes + 1 hour chilling + 10 minutes baking.

These are much nicer than the bought variety, and make a small can of salmon go a long way, so why not make double quantity, and save some for another time?

Pesce Italiano

Bread and Butter Fish Pie

Fish Cobbler

2 tablespoons dried sliced onions, crushed

350 g (12 oz) potatoes, boiled and mashed

234 g can salmon, skin and any bones removed, drained and flaked

2 tablespoons tomato ketchup

2 teaspoons dried parsley

flour for dusting

1 medium egg

1 tablespoon skimmed milk

6 tablespoons dried breadcrumbs

salt and freshly ground black pepper

1 Simmer the dried onion in boiling water for 5 minutes and drain well.

2 Mix with the potato, salmon, ketchup, parsley and seasoning.

3 Put mixture on a floured plate and chill for at least 1 hour.

4 Preheat the oven to Gas Mark 6/200°C/ 400°F.

5 Beat the egg with the skimmed milk.

6 Flour your hands and shape the mixture into 4 patties. Dip each into the egg and milk mixture, and coat with breadcrumbs.

7 Bake for 10 minutes and serve immediately.

Cook's tip

If you crush the dried onion, it comes out much finer than chopped fresh onion and needs no further cooking.

Variation

Use tuna canned in brine, instead of salmon. The Points per serving will be 7½. Calories will be 410.

3½ Points per serving

14 Total Points per recipe

255 Calories per serving

4 Servings

Freezing not recommended. Preparation time: 15 minutes + 20 minutes standing + 30 minutes cooking.

This is a new twist on an old family favourite. It's also an excellent way to use up stale bread and have that lovely low-Calorie, high-protein fish.

6 thin slices wholemeal bread

4 teaspoons low-fat spread

6 thin pieces of white fish (about 450 g/1 lb)

1 small onion, chopped

1 tablespoon lemon juice

1 egg

300 ml (½ pint) skimmed milk

1 Preheat the oven to Gas Mark 5/190°C/ 375°F.

2 Leave the crusts on the bread and lightly spread the low-fat spread over it. Cut bread into triangles.

3 Take half the fish and lay it in the base of a shallow ovenproof dish. Sprinkle with half the onion and a little lemon juice.

4 Arrange half the bread over the top.

5 Repeat with the rest of the fish, onion and lemon juice. Finish with the rest of the bread.

6 Lightly beat the egg and mix with the milk. Pour the mixture over the bread and leave for 20 minutes to allow it to soak in.

7 Bake in the oven for 30 minutes.

4 Points per serving

15½ Total Points per recipe

300 Calories per serving

4 Servings

Freezing not recommended. Preparation time: 15 minutes + 25 minutes cooking. This is a great supper dish for when friends come round for the evening. Serve with crisp green salad.

400 g (14 oz) canned chopped tomatoes with onion

225 g (8 oz) white fish, cubed

225 g (8 oz) smoked fish, cubed

8 × 2.5 cm (1-inch) slices french bread

2 teaspoons low-fat spread

50 g (1¾ oz) half-fat Cheddar, grated

1 Preheat the oven to Gas Mark 6/200°C/400°F.

2 Put the tomatoes in a saucepan and gently heat.

3 Add the fish and cook for 5–8 minutes.

4 Spread the french bread with the low-fat spread.

5 Put the fish mixture in an ovenproof dish and arrange the french bread over the top. Sprinkle with grated cheese.

6 Bake in the oven for 25 minutes.

Pesto Haddock

3½ Points per serving

7 Total Points per recipe

175 Calories per serving

2 Servings

Freezing not recommended. Preparation and cooking time: 15 minutes.
You could also try some of the exotic species such as swordfish or tuna. Adjust the Points accordingly. Swordfish will be 225 Calories per serving and tuna will be 275 Calories per serving. This dish goes well with pasta.

lemon juice
2 × 175 g (6 oz) frozen haddock steaks
1 tablespoon red pesto
25 g (1 oz) fresh breadcrumbs

1 Preheat the grill.
2 Sprinkle lemon juice on the haddock and grill on one side for about 5 minutes.
3 Turn over and spread with red pesto.
4 Top with breadcrumbs and grill for further 5 minutes until the fish is cooked.

 ## Family Fish Pie

5 Points per serving

20 Total Points per recipe

295 Calories per serving

4 Servings

Freezing not recommended. Preparation time: 30 minutes + 25 minutes baking.
This all-in-one supper dish is sure to be popular with all the family, and it's very simple to prepare.

low-fat cooking spray
4 × 100 g (3½ oz) frozen haddock steaks
100 g (3½ oz) frozen prawns, defrosted
150 g (5½ oz) frozen peas and sweetcorn, lightly cooked and drained
295 g can 99% fat-free condensed mushroom soup
600 g (1 lb 5 oz) potatoes, boiled, mashed and seasoned
salt and freshly ground black pepper

Pesto Haddock

1 Preheat the oven to Gas Mark 5/190°C/ 375°F.

2 Spray an ovenproof dish a couple of times with low-fat cooking spray.

3 Put the haddock steaks in the dish.

4 Mix the prawns, peas and sweetcorn with the mushroom soup and spoon over the haddock. Season with salt and black pepper.

5 Top with the mashed potatoes and bake for 25 minutes, or until fish is cooked. Serve immediately.

Variations

Top the fish and condensed soup mixture with 25 g (1 oz) fresh wholemeal bread-crumbs and 25 g (1 oz) half-fat Cheddar cheese, grated: add 20 Calories and 1 Point per serving. Serve the potatoes separately.

Use cod steaks instead of haddock. Calories and Points will be the same.

 ## Spaghetti Vongole

5 Points per serving

10 Total Points per recipe

330 Calories per serving

2 Servings

Freezing not recommended. Preparation and cooking time: 20 minutes.
This couldn't be simpler to make, and makes a nice change from traditional Spaghetti Bolognese.

100 g (3½ oz) spaghetti or other dried pasta
290 g can baby clams in brine, drained
400 g (14 oz) canned chopped tomatoes with garlic and herbs
salt and freshly ground black pepper

1 Cook the pasta in plenty of boiling, salted water for 12–15 minutes and drain well.

2 While it's cooking, heat the clams gently with the chopped tomatoes. Season with salt and plenty of black pepper.

3 Serve the pasta with the sauce poured over it.

Cook's tip

Traditionally the Italians don't serve parmesan cheese with a seafood pasta dish, but if you want it, why not have it? But remember to add the extra Points.

Variation

If you can't get baby clams, use prawns instead. The Points remain the same. Calories will be 255 per serving.

 ## Cod Parcels

2 Points per serving

8 Total Points per recipe

165 Calories per serving

4 Servings

Freezing not recommended. Preparation and cooking time: 20 minutes.
A delicious dish, and very simple to do if you're on your own.

low-fat cooking spray
4 × 175 g (6 oz) cod fillets
125 g (4½ oz) broccoli
2 carrots, sliced
salt and freshly ground black pepper

1 Take 4 pieces of foil and spray very lightly with low-fat cooking spray.

2 Put a piece of fish on each one.

3 Share out the broccoli florets and carrot between each parcel and place on top of the fish. Season to taste.

4 Secure each parcel by folding the foil around the fish and vegetables, and steam for 10 minutes or until the fish is cooked.

Cook's tip

If you're cooking this in the microwave use baking parchment to make the parcels.

It's not easy keeping to just three meals a day while the rest of the world tucks into a few morsels before dinner is cooked or when the children come back from school. So this completely new chapter offers plenty of ideas for indulging without feeling guilty. You will be amazed at how treats like Luxury Jaffa Cakes and Chocolate Oranges can all be part of your new healthy way of eating.

Keep simple ingredients in your store-cupboard. Instant cup-a-soup will be handy for the French Cup-a-Soup recipe, and a jar of Marmite will help you conjure up the Marmite Beanie Toasties. You'll even be able to crunch your way through Micro-Magic Tattie Crisps – these heavenly treats are an absolute must if you just can't kick the nibbling habit.

snacks

and nibbles

 Luxury Jaffa Cakes

V

6½ Points per serving

13 Total Points per recipe

240 Calories per serving

2 Servings

Freezing not recommended. Preparation time: 5–10 minutes.

On days when you've just got to have something chocolatey, try these melt-in-your-mouth goodies.

8 Jaffa cake biscuits
1 carton Weight Watchers from Heinz
  Chocolate Mousse
4 teaspoons desiccated coconut

1 Sandwich together two Jaffa cakes, chocolate side in, with 1–2 teaspoons of the mousse.

2 Roll the edges of the 'sandwiches' in the coconut: the mousse filling will pick up the coconut. Repeat with the rest of the ingredients.

Peach and Banana Smoothie

V

5 Points per serving

265 Calories per serving

1 Serving

Freezing not recommended. Preparation time: 5–10 minutes.

1 medium ripe banana
1 tablespoon Greek-style natural
  yogurt, chilled
200 ml (7 fl oz) semi-skimmed milk,
  chilled
2 teaspoons honey
4 slices canned peaches
pulp of one passion fruit (optional)

1 Place all the ingredients except the passion fruit in a food processor or blender and process until smooth. Alternatively, place them in a bowl and beat together.

2 Stir in the passion fruit pulp (if using) and pour into a tall glass.

Frozen Fruit Chunks

V

1½ Points per serving

100 Calories per serving

1 Serving

Freezing recommended. Preparation time: 5 minutes + freezing.

This is a nice change from a whole piece of fresh fruit, bite-sized treats of frozen fruit neatly threaded on cocktail sticks. I cheated by buying a tub of Blue Skies tropical fruit. You can find chopped mango and pineapple in supermarkets if you don't feel like all the peeling and chopping.

4 cubes (100 g/3½ oz) of chopped
  mango
4 cubes (100 g/3½ oz) of fresh chopped
  pineapple or 4 canned pineapple
  chunks, drained

1 Place the chunks of fruit in individual spaces of an ice-cube tray. Stick a cocktail stick into each piece and freeze.

2 Remove the fruit from the tray and allow to thaw only slightly before eating from the cocktail sticks.

Variations

When you really feel like indulging, try dipping the frozen fruit in melted chocolate. Alternatively, serve the frozen chunks as ice cubes with your favourite low-calorie drink. Add the extra Points.

 ## Sesame Fingers

Ⓥ

4 Points per serving

100 Calories per serving

1 Serving

Freezing not recommended. Preparation time: 5 minutes.

Think sponge fingers are only good for soaking and using in trifle? Then think again. This sticky sweet indulgence shows how to liven up those fingers in a matter of minutes.

2 teaspoons runny honey

3 sponge fingers

½ teaspoon sesame seeds

1 Spread the honey evenly over one side of the sponge fingers.

2 Sprinkle the sesame seeds on top.

 ## Stuffed Festive Prunes

Ⓥ

3 Points per serving

6 Total Points per recipe

150 Calories per serving

2 Servings

Freezing not recommended. Preparation and cooking time: 20 minutes.

10 stoned prunes

200 ml (7 fl oz) orange juice

1 cinnamon stick

½ teaspoon mixed spice

10 walnut halves

a few bits of crystallised ginger

1 Stew the prunes in the orange juice, cinnamon and mixed spice until soft.

2 Stuff each prune with a walnut half and then let the prunes soak in the cooking juices for about 10 minutes.

3 Warm through gently and serve, topped with the ginger.

Variation

You can use fresh or dried dates, but you may find the dates difficult to stuff, so simply serve with the walnuts.

Weight Watchers tip

Save on Points by using walnut quarters.

 ## Croque Monsieur aux Tomates

2½ Points per serving

160 Calories per serving

1 Serving

Freezing not recommended. Preparation and cooking time: 5 minutes.

1 medium slice white bread from an 800 g loaf

4 cherry tomatoes, sliced

1 thin slice lean ham

1 low-fat cheese slice

salt and freshly ground black pepper

1 Preheat the grill.

2 Cover the bread with sliced tomatoes and grill for 2 minutes.

3 Season with salt and pepper, add the ham and top with the cheese.

4 Grill for a further minute or so until golden brown and bubbling, and serve immediately.

Variation

For a crisper 'croque' toast the bread on one side before adding the tomatoes to the untoasted side. Proceed as above.

Chocolate Oranges

(v)

1 Point per serving

2 Total Points per recipe

60 Calories per serving

2 Servings

Freezing not recommended. Preparation time: 5–10 minutes.

Fresh fruit is great, but there are times when you fancy fruit with a bit of a twist. So how about trying these mint-chocolate covered oranges? The crumbs of peppermint Aero give an amazing taste and texture to fresh segments of orange.

1 orange, peeled and split into segments

1 mini peppermint Aero bar

2 teaspoons Light Greek-style natural yogurt

1 Remove as much pith as you can from the orange. Place the segments in two individual glass bowls.

2 Finely grate the chocolate on top of the orange.

3 Spoon the yogurt on top and serve.

Cook's tip

This is best prepared just before serving.

Weight Watchers tip

If you can't get the light version of Greek-style yogurt, try a low-fat fromage frais or use ordinary Greek-style yogurt.

Chocolate Oranges

 ### Dried Fruit Fool

 ### Chilli Crackers

 ### Instant Chocolate Cheesecake

V

2½ Points per serving

110 Calories per serving

1 Serving

Freezing not recommended. Preparation time: 5 minutes + chilling.

125 ml (4 fl oz) pot low-fat plain yogurt
2 teaspoons raisins
1 teaspoon dried mixed peel
a sprinkling of desiccated coconut

1 Mix the yogurt with the raisins and dried mixed peel.
2 Sprinkle the coconut on top and serve chilled.

V

1 Point per serving

60 Calories per serving

1 Serving

Freezing not recommended. Preparation and cooking time: 5 minutes.
There are times when you just fancy something crisp to munch on, and crispbreads and plain crackers just seem too boring. Try spicing up uneven pieces of cream crackers with this simple recipe. A microwave is best for this, though it does work under the grill with some careful watching!

2 cream crackers, broken into bite-sized
pieces
a few drops of lemon juice
a generous pinch of chilli powder

1 Flavour the crackers with lemon juice and chilli powder (as hot as you dare!) and place on a microwaveable plate.
2 Microwave on high for 1 minute and then cool to allow them to crisp up.

V

1½ Points per cheesecake

10½ Total Points per cheesecake

65 Calories per serving

8 Cheesecakes

Freezing not recommended. Preparation time: 5–10 minutes.
A speedy treat that's surprisingly low in Points.

2 teaspoons light Philadelphia soft
cheese
6 teaspoons low-fat fromage frais
8 Jaffa cakes
1 treat-size Cadbury's flake

1 Mix the soft cheese with the fromage frais.
2 Spread a teaspoon of this cheese mixture over the chocolate side of each Jaffa cake.
3 Crumble the flake on top and serve.

Frozen Fruit Chunks **Page 154**

 Crispbread Creams

V

1 Point per serving

2 Total Points per recipe

75 Calories per serving

2 Servings

Freezing not recommended. Preparation time: 5 minutes.

Convert a crunchy ready-made crisped roll into a scrumptious treat in just 5 minutes.

2 teaspoons Greek-style plain yogurt
2 toasted Swedish Krisproll
2 teaspoons reduced-sugar strawberry
jam

1 Spread the yogurt evenly over the two rolls and top generously with the jam.

Mackerel Pâté

4 Points per serving

8½ Total Points per recipe

200 Calories per serving

2 Servings

Freezing recommended. Preparation time: 10 minutes + chilling.
Delicious with wholemeal bread or toast. Add the extra Points

1 cooked smoked mackerel fillet
(weighing about 100 g/3½ oz)
75 g (2¾ oz) low-fat fromage frais
1 tablespoon chopped fresh chives
2 teaspoons lemon juice
a pinch of cayenne pepper

1 Remove the skin from the fish. Break the flesh into small pieces and mash with a fork. Remove any bones.

2 Mix together the fromage frais, chives, lemon juice and cayenne pepper.

3 Blend the fish with this mixture using a fork. Serve chilled.

 Cinnamon Crumpet

V

1½ Points per serving

105 Calories per serving

1 Serving

Freezing not recommended. Preparation and cooking time: 5 minutes.
This sweet treat needs no butter or jam and can be made very quickly

1 teaspoon sugar
¼ teaspoon cinnamon
1 crumpet

1 Preheat the grill to very hot.

2 Mix the sugar and cinnamon and sprinkle on the crumpet.

3 Flash under the hot grill until the sugar starts to bubble.

Cook's tip

Be very careful not to burn your mouth on the hot sugar.

Variation

Mixed spice could be used instead of cinnamon.

Peach Toasts

Ⓥ

2 Points per serving

130 Calories per serving

① Serving

Freezing not recommended. Preparation time: 5 minutes.

3 slices Melba Toast
25 g (1 oz) Heinz Sandwich Spread (any flavour)
50 g (1¾ oz) canned peach slices in natural juice, drained

1 Spread the toasts with the sandwich spread.
2 Top with the peach slices.

Cook's tip

Make sure the peaches are well drained or the toasts will go soggy.

Variation

You could add some wafer-thin ham or turkey – don't forget to alter the Points.

 ## Pitta Salad

Ⓥ

2 Points per serving

8½ Total Points per recipe

150 Calories per serving

④ Servings

Freezing not recommended. Preparation time: 15 minutes.
In the Middle East bread is often used in salads. It makes them more substantial and soaks up the juices and dressing. This is one version, but experiment with some ideas of your own.

Try to use cherry tomatoes for this recipe as they are so much sweeter, and look impressive.

25 g (1 oz) sunflower seeds
about 75 g (2¾ oz) mixed salad leaves, shredded
2 medium pitta breads, lightly toasted and cut into 1 cm (½-inch) squares
4 tomatoes, chopped or 8 ripe cherry tomatoes, halved
25 g (1 oz) sultanas
2 tablespoons fat-free french salad dressing or to taste

1 Toast the sunflower seeds gently under a medium grill until brown. Shake occasionally to ensure they cook evely. Don't leave them as they burn very quickly!
2 Mix together the salad leaves, pitta bread, tomatoes, sultanas, and sunflower seeds.
3 Add some fat-free french salad dressing and toss the salad.
4 Let the salad stand for about 5 minutes so the bread soaks up the flavours.

 ## French Cup-a-Soup

2 Points per serving

135 Calories per serving

① Serving

Freezing not recommended. Preparation time: 5 minutes.

1 sachet low-calorie cup-a-soup
a thin spread of mustard
1 Melba Toast
25 g (1 oz) half-fat Cheddar cheese, grated.

1 Make up the low-calorie cup-a-soup with boiling water.
2 Spread the mustard onto the Melba Toast and place the grated cheese on top.
3 Float the cheesy Melba Toast in the soup, and let the soup soak into the bread for 1 minute before eating.

Weight Watchers tip

Low-calorie cup-a-soups are ideal when you need a hot, filling drink.

Variations

Try a variety of different soup flavours and use Marmite instead of mustard for a change.

2-minute Trifle

v

4 Points per serving

11½ Total Points per recipe

190 Calories per serving

3 Servings

Freezing not recommended. Preparation time: 5 minutes.

1 small banana, sliced
3 × 25 g (1 oz) slices of jam Swiss roll
3 tbsp aerosol cream

1 Put a layer of banana slices over each slice of Swiss roll.
2 Squirt a little aerosol cream on top and serve immediately.

2-minute Trifle

Marshmallow and Chocolate Float

v

2½ Points per serving

80 Calories per serving

1 Serving

Freezing not recommended. Preparation time: 5 minutes.

1 sachet Cadbury's Chocolate Options
6 mini marshmallows
a dusting of cocoa powder

1 Make a piping-hot mug of Chocolate Options. Top with marshmallows and cocoa powder.

2-minute Popcorn

Ⓥ

1 Point per serving

3 Total Points per recipe

55 Calories per serving

❸ Servings

Freezing not recommended. Preparation time: 5 minutes.

A healthy high-fibre snack. Bought popcorn can be high in Points, so make sure you always have some popping corn in the cupboard for days when only something crunchy will do.

1 teaspoon corn oil
2 heaped tablespoons popping corn

1 Heat a non-stick pan with a lid. Pour in the oil and maintain on a high heat.
2 Add the corn and cover. The corn should start to pop and hit the lid. Remove from the heat once the popping stops.

Weight Watchers tip
To cut down on fat even further, try pouring off a little oil once it is heated, before you add the corn. Or add another dessertspoon of corn and make enough popcorn to serve 4.

Variation
Add a good pinch of chilli powder to the oil to make spicy popcorn.

Bananarama Grill

Ⓥ

2 Points per serving

4 Total Points per recipe

125 Calories per serving

❷ Servings

Freezing not recommended. Preparation time: 5 minutes.
Tim Henman goes bananas over bananas. "There's no better source of energy," he'll tell you, so this snack is great for when you're feeling like you're flagging.

2 medium slices wholemeal bread
1 small banana, mashed
2 teaspoons caster sugar

1 Preheat the grill.
2 Spread the bread with the mashed banana.
3 Sprinkle with the caster sugar and grill for a minute or 2 until the sugar melts.
4 Eat straightaway.

 ## Marmite Beanie Toasties

Ⓥ

1½ Points per serving

7 Total Points per recipe

140 Calories per serving

❹ Servings

Freezing not recommended. Preparation time: 10 minutes.
Beans on toast make an ideal snack when you're in a hurry or just feeling greedy. Served this way, with a thin layer of Marmite, they're even more moreish!

4 medium slices wholemeal bread
   toasted
4 teaspoons Marmite
420 g can Weight Watchers from Heinz
   Baked Beans, heated

1 Spread each slice of toast with a teaspoonful of Marmite.
2 Top with the beans and serve immediately.

Cook's tip
You can substitute Vecon or Bovril for the Marmite.

 ## Carrot Dip

V

½ Point per serving

2 Total Points per recipe

45 Calories per serving

4 Servings

Freezing not recommended. Preparation and cooking time: 20 minutes + 1 hour chilling.

Here is a dip with a difference – a purée of cooked carrot blended with plain yogurt and lightly spiced! Very moreish. Serve with a selection of vegetables (celery, red and green peppers, courgettes, radishes, cauliflower and mushrooms) and mini breadsticks.

225 g (8 oz) carrots, sliced and cooked until just tender
1 garlic clove, crushed
½ teaspoon ground coriander
200 g (7 oz) low-fat plain yogurt
cayenne
salt

1 Put the cooked carrots in a blender or food processor with the garlic, coriander and yogurt. Purée until smooth.

2 Season with cayenne and salt. Mix and leave in the fridge for 1 hour to let the flavours develop.

Cook's tip
Frozen carrots could be used; simply defrost them and blend. If you cook them they will lose all flavour.

Weight Watchers tip
Carrot Dip is an ideal party food, along with Cocktail Nibbles (right), Prawn Toasties (page 13) and Exotic Dip (page 14).

 ## Cocktail Nibbles

Calculate the Total Points according to your choices from the list below.

Freezing not recommended. Preparation time: 45 minutes.

These can be made in advance so you don't need to spend hours in the kitchen during a party. As a rough guide, you need to prepare 8–12 sticks per person at a party and 2–3 sticks if serving them as the first course to a meal.

Skewer a selection of the following on cocktail sticks.

• 100 g (3½ oz) smoked wafer-thin turkey or ham wrapped around ½ cherry tomato or tomato quarter: 2 Points/125 Calories

• ham pinwheels made by spreading 100 g (3½ oz) lean ham with 25 g (1 oz) low-fat cheese spread, rolling it up and slicing into pinwheels: 2½ Points/190 Calories

• 100 g (3½ oz) cooked chicken tikka, cut into small cubes: 3 Points/145 Calories

• 250 g canned pineapple cubes in natural juice: 1½ Points/90 Calories

• 250 g mini beetroots, quartered if large: 0 Points/115 Calories

• 100 g (3½ oz) silverskin onions: 0 Points/25 Calories

• 100 g (3½ oz) cubes of cucumber: 0 Points/10 Calories

• 100 g (3½ oz) jumbo prawns, soaked in lemon juice and sprinkled with a touch of chilli powder: 2 Points/100 Calories

Cook's tip
Buy coloured cocktail sticks with decorations on top to liven up the display.

Carrot Dip
Cocktail Nibbles

Micro-Magic Tattie Crisps

(V)

1½ Points per serving

135 Calories per serving

❶ Serving (makes about 25 crisps)

Freezing not recommended. Preparation time: 5 minutes + 10 minutes cooking + 10 minutes cooling.

They're tasty, they're tempting, they're totally fat-free. So, make your own potato crisps in minutes. It couldn't be simpler!

150 g (5½ oz) potato
salt or Lo-Salt to taste

1 Peel the potato and with a potato peeler shave off very thin slices.
2 Blot the slices with kitchen paper to get rid of any excess moisture.
3 Arrange the potato slices in a single layer on a microwavable plate and in the microwave cook on high (see tip) for 2 minutes.
4 Leave to stand, with the microwave door open, for 2 minutes, then cook on high for a further 2 minutes.
5 Repeat Step 4, allow to cool for about 10 minutes, and add salt or Lo-Salt to taste.

Cook's tips

The potato can also be sliced with the fine blade of a food processor (this can be done in seconds).

Timings are based on a 650 watt oven. On a higher wattage, you could probably cook for 30 seconds less – this really is just a matter of trial and error.

The crisps can also be made in a conventional oven. Cook on the top shelf at Gas Mark 5/190°C/375°F for about 6 minutes. Oven temperatures vary, so you simply have to keep opening the door and wait for the moment when they are golden and crispy.

Terrific Telly Tempters

(V)

1½ Points per serving

65 Calories per serving

❶ Serving

Freezing not recommended. Preparation time: 5–10 minutes.

Lovely, isn't it, when you can eat as much as you like of something, and know that it's actually doing you good? These little 'telly tempters' taste fab and it's worth keeping a permanent supply of them in the fridge.

Serve with any fresh vegetables from the free list – e.g. cherry tomatoes, radishes, chopped celery, green and red peppers.

125 ml small carton low-fat plain yogurt
1 spring onion, chopped finely
1 tablespoon chopped fresh mint or
*   ½ teaspoon dried mint*

1 Mix the yogurt, spring onion and mint in a small bowl.
2 Sit back and enjoy!

Quick Mozzarella Pizza

6 Points per serving

22½ Total Points per serving

270 Calories per serving

④ Servings

Freezing not recommended. Preparation
time: 10 minutes + 15 minutes cooking.

4 mini pittas
4 teaspoons tomato purée
4 tomatoes, sliced
210 g (7 oz) mozzarella cheese, sliced
30 g (1 oz) canned anchovies, drained
    and patted dry
6 large olives, pitted and cut in slivers
1 tablespoon chopped fresh oregano, or
    1½ teaspoons dried oregano
salt and freshly ground black pepper

1 Preheat the oven to Gas Mark 5/190°C/
375°F.
2 Place the pittas on a baking sheet and
brush a teaspoon of tomato purée over the
surface of each one.
3 Arrange the tomatoes and mozzarella
cheese on top of the pittas in an
overlapping layer. Top with the anchovies
and olives and sprinkle with oregano.
Season with salt and pepper.
4 Bake in an oven for 15–20 minutes,
until cooked and golden.

Worried about whether you've got time to get the apron on and start baking? With these recipes you won't need any special skills or fancy moulds and you can bake up a delightful dish in around 30 minutes. For super-easy baking, try the Chocolate-iced Fairy Cakes (which use a cake mix) or the no-bake Crunchy Fruit Fingers. But on days when you feel more adventurous, check out the Hazelnut Cake and Cheat's Swiss Roll. For impressing your guests, the Brandy Snap Baskets and Arctic Butterflies are a must. And we haven't forgotten those seasonal favourites, Easter Biscuits and good old Christmas cake. No doubt this chapter's going to get a bit dog-eared.

cakes

and bakes

 **Fruit Loaf**

Ⓥ

1½ Points per serving

36 Total Points per recipe

85 Calories per serving

㉓ Servings (25 g/1 oz each)

Freezing recommended. Preparation time: 20 minutes + overnight soaking + 1 hour cooking.

Be warned! This juicy fruit loaf is very more-ish. You shouldn't need any spread, it's so moist, but if you must have some, try it with Weight Watchers from Heinz Olivite – and remember to add those extra Points!

350 g (12 oz) mixed fruit
175 g (6 oz) dark brown sugar
200 ml (7 fl oz) cold tea
1 egg
225 g (8 oz) self-raising flour + a little
   extra for dusting

1 Put the mixed fruit and sugar in a bowl and add the cold tea.

2 Cover with cling film and leave to soak overnight.

3 Preheat the oven to Gas Mark 6/200°C/ 400°F.

4 Line a 1 kg/2 lb loaf tin with greaseproof paper and dust lightly with flour.

5 Add the egg and the flour to the fruit mixture and mix well.

6 Pour into the loaf tin and bake for 1 hour in the centre of the oven.

7 Remove from the oven, peel the greaseproof paper off gently and leave to cool on a wire rack.

 **Lemon Triangles**

Ⓥ

2 Points per triangle

38 Total Points per recipe

115 Calories per triangle

⑱ Triangles

Freezing not recommended. Preparation time: 30 minutes + chilling.

These lemony bites are wonderful with coffee and could even be topped with low-fat lemon mousse and served as a dessert.

25 g (1 oz) soft brown sugar
75 g (2¾ oz) reduced-fat spread,
   e.g. Krona
6 tablespoons condensed skimmed milk
zest and juice of 1 unwaxed lemon
225 g (8 oz) reduced-fat digestive
   biscuits, crushed

For the topping

4 tablespoons icing sugar

1 Take a 18 cm (7-inch) square cake tin about 2.5cm (1 inch) deep and line with greaseproof paper.

2 Melt the sugar and reduced-fat spread and add the condensed skimmed milk. Cook gently for 3 minutes.

3 Add 1 tablespoon of the lemon juice, the zest and the crushed biscuits. Mix.

4 Press into the tin and chill in the fridge.

5 Make the icing. Gradually add about 1 tablespoon boiling water and the remainder of the lemon juice to the icing sugar. Be careful as it needs very little water. You want a smooth paste of a consistency that will slowly drop off the back of a spoon and that will coat the triangles.

6 Turn out the chilled base. Turn it upside-down and coat the bottom with the lemon icing (this gives a much smoother surface). Chill again and divide into 18 small triangles.

Cook's tip

Crush the biscuits by putting them in a large freezer bag (with no holes!) and rolling them gently with a rolling pin. You want crumbs that are of uneven size – this gives a much more interesting texture.

Variation

Use orange instead of lemon.

Arctic Butterflies

v

1½ Points per cake

17½ Total Points per recipe

90 Calories per cake

12 Cakes

Freezing not recommended. Preparation time 15 minutes + 15 minutes baking.

225 g (8 oz) packet McDougalls Low-Fat Sponge Mix

1 medium egg

125 ml (4 fl oz) water

For the decoration

1 scoop Weight Watchers from Heinz Ice Cream

1 Preheat the oven to Gas Mark 6/200°C/400°F.

2 Put the sponge mix into a bowl and add the egg and 4 dessertspoons of water. Mix well, and then beat for 2 minutes.

3 Add the rest of the water and beat for a further minute. Spoon into paper cake cases placed on a baking sheet.

4 Bake for 10–12 minutes until lightly golden and firm. Cool on a wire tray.

5 With a sharp knife carefully cut a thin slice off the top of each cake. Cut these slices into two.

6 Scoop a teaspoonful of ice cream on to the top. Make wings on top of the ice cream with the halved slices of cake. Serve immediately.

Arctic Butterflies

 **Ginger Biscuits**

Ⓥ

½ Point per biscuit

11 Total Points per recipe

40 Calories per biscuit

㉑ Biscuits

Freezing not recommended. Preparation time: 25 minutes + 12 minutes baking.

100 g (3½ oz) plain flour
¾ teaspoon salt
1 teaspoon baking powder
1 teaspoon sodium bicarbonate
1 teaspoon ginger powder
1 teaspoon mixed spice
50 g (1¾ oz) reduced-fat spread
50 g (1¾ oz) demerara sugar
1 tablespoon syrup, warmed
50 ml (2 fl oz) skimmed milk

1 Preheat the oven to Gas Mark 4/180°C/350°F.

2 Sift the flour, salt, baking powder, sodium bicarbonate, ginger powder and mixed spice into a large bowl and rub in the reduced-fat spread until it resembles breadcrumbs.

3 Add the sugar, warmed syrup and milk and mix.

4 Spoon little heaps of the mixture – about the size of a 10p piece – on to a non-stick baking tray. The mixture spreads when cooking, so make sure the biscuits are placed well apart.

5 Bake for 12 minutes and allow to cool on the tray before removing. A sharp knife slid under the biscuits will loosen them.

 Cherry Cheesecake

Ⓥ

5 Points per serving

39 Total Points per recipe

260 Calories per serving

⑧ Servings

Freezing not recommended. Preparation and cooking time: 30 minutes + chilling. This quick and easy cheesecake has a delicious topping of cherries. However it's a little extravagant on the Points so keep it for special occasions.

75 g (2¾ oz) reduced-fat spread,
*   e.g. Krona*
225 g (8 oz) reduced-fat digestive
*   biscuits, crushed (see page 170)*
125 g (4½ oz) low-fat soft cheese
100 g (3½ oz) low-fat plain fromage frais
75 g (2¾ oz) icing sugar
420 g canned black cherries, drained
*   and stoned*

1 Line an 18 cm (7-inch) loose-bottomed cake tin with greaseproof paper.

2 Melt the reduced-fat spread and add the crushed biscuits.

3 Mix and press into the base of the cake tin with your fingers. Chill.

4 Mix the low-fat soft cheese and fromage frais together. Beat in the icing sugar.

5 Spread over the cold biscuit base and top with cherries.

Variation

You can use any fruit to top the cheesecake – try a tropical cheesecake with tinned or fresh pineapple, mango and passion fruit.

Cherry Cheesecake

 ## Hazelnut Cake

(V)

3 Points per serving

24 Total Points per recipe

195 Calories per serving

8 Servings

Freezing not recommended. Preparation time: 15 minutes + 30 minutes baking + cooling.

This is an impressive and unusual cake – ideal as a dessert when entertaining. You can make it in advance, though the chocolatey filling needs to be added just before serving. Your guests won't believe it took only about 15 minutes and they can indulge with a clear conscience!

3 egg whites
175 g (6 oz) caster sugar
1 teaspoon baking powder
100 g (3½ oz) ground hazelnuts

For the filling and decoration

2 × 55 g pots low-calorie Chocolate
*   Mousse*
100 g (3½ oz) canned pears in natural
*   juice or fresh peeled pears, sliced*
*   thinly*
icing sugar

1 Preheat the oven to Gas Mark 3/170°C/ 320°F.

2 Line two 18 cm (7-inch) non-stick cake tins with greaseproof paper.

3 Beat the egg whites stiffly.

4 Mix in the sugar, baking powder and hazelnuts gently, using a metal spoon. Divide the mixture between the tins.

5 Bake for 30 minutes.

6 Turn out the cakes on to a wire rack to cool (you may need to loosen the sides carefully with a knife).

7 When cool, remove the greaseproof paper gently. Don't worry if a little of the bottom comes away with the paper.

8 Immediately before serving, turn one of the cakes upside down. Spread the chocolate mousse on the upturned base and add a thin layer of pears.

9 Place the other cake on top (with the crunchy top uppermost) and sprinkle with sieved icing sugar.

 ## Cottage Cheese Drop Scones

1 Point per scone

12 Total Points per recipe

40 Calories per scone

16 Scones

Freezing not recommended. Preparation time: 30 minutes + 30 minutes standing. These are ideal if unexpected company drop in. This is also a good easy recipe for children to make.

25 g (1 oz) vegetable margarine
100 g (3½ oz) plain cottage cheese
2 eggs, lightly beaten
50 g (1¾ oz) wholemeal flour
3 tablespoons skimmed milk
low-fat cooking spray

1 Melt the margarine and add the cottage cheese.

2 Beat in the eggs and flour and finally the milk. Leave to stand for ½ hour.

3 Lightly spray a good frying pan with low-fat cooking spray and drop spoonfuls of the mixture on to the frying pan allowing the mixture to spread.

4 When bubbles appear on the surface turn the scones with a palette knife and cook on the other side. Serve immediately.

Brandy Snap Baskets

(V)

3½ Points per serving

15 Total Points per recipe

165 Calories per serving

4 Servings

Freezing not recommended. Preparation time: 5 minutes.

Brandy snaps always remind me of Christmas and this recipe makes a delicious change from the heavy meals of the festive season. The two different colours of mousse, side-by-side look impressive. Serve with ready-made chocolate cake decorations (like the chocolate leaves made by Lee's), finish with a dusting of icing sugar 'snow'.

2 Shape Sunshine Mousse (one lemon and lime flavour, one pink grapefruit)
4 brandy snap baskets
1 large can Fruitini fruit pieces (pineapple, peaches or fruit salad are fine)

1 Spoon 1 tablespoon of the white lemon-and-lime mousse and 1 tablespoon of the pink grapefruit mousse into each brandy snap basket.
2 Top with Fruitini fruit pieces.

Cook's tip
Brandy snap coronets are also available.

Variations
Pre-set sugar-free jelly and fruit, or a thick low-fat fruit yogurt could be used instead of the mousse. Points remain the same.

Cheat's Swiss Roll

(V)

2½ Points per serving

19½ Total Points per recipe

130 Calories per serving

8 Servings

Freezing recommended. Preparation and cooking time: 25 minutes.

3 eggs
75 g (2¾ oz) caster sugar
75 g (2¾ oz) self-raising flour
50 g (1¾ oz) green seedless grapes, halved
1 kiwi fruit, peeled and chopped
125 g half-fat crème fraîche

1 Grease and line a 23 × 33 cm (9 × 13-inch) swiss roll tin. Preheat the oven to Gas Mark 7/220°C/425°F.
2 Whisk together the eggs and caster sugar until very thick and creamy. This takes 5 minutes with an electric mixer.
3 Carefully mix in the flour and pour into the swiss roll tin. Bake for 8 minutes until lightly brown and 'springy' to the touch.
4 Lay a sheet of greaseproof paper over a damp tea towel. Sprinkle caster sugar over the paper.
5 Turn the cake out onto the paper and gently roll up the cake with the paper inside. Allow to cool.
6 Mix the fruit with the crème fraîche.
7 Carefully unroll the cake – don't try to get it completely flat. Spread the crème fraîche mixture over evenly. Gently roll up the cake again.

 ## Cinnamon and Orange Scones

(V)

2½ Points per scone

19½ Total Points per recipe

145 Calories per scone

8 Scones

Freezing recommended. Preparation and cooking time: 30 minutes.

Have these by the fire on Christmas Eve or New Year's Eve before all the celebrations begin.

200 g (7 oz) wholemeal flour
1 teaspoon ground cinnamon
50 g (1¾ oz) hard margarine
25 g (1 oz) caster sugar
grated zest of 1 orange
125 ml (4 fl oz) skimmed milk

1 Preheat the oven to Gas Mark 7/220°C/425°F. Sieve together the flour and cinnamon.
2 Rub in the margarine (the mixture should resemble breadcrumbs). Add the sugar and orange zest.
3 Add the milk gradually and stop when you have a soft dough, even if all the milk hasn't been used up.
4 Roll out to a thickness of 1 cm (½ inch) and cut into rounds with a 5 cm (2-inch) cutter.
5 Bake for 10 minutes until risen and lightly brown

Cook's tip
Dip the cutter in flour if you find it sticks.

Cheat's Swiss Roll
Brandy Snap Baskets

 **Winter Fruit Bread**

Ⓥ

3 Points per slice

57 Total Points per recipe

175 Calories per slice

㉑ Slices

Freezing recommended. Preparation time: 40 minutes + 4 hours rising + 50 minutes baking.

This is a great recipe for getting rid of pent-up aggression if the weight isn't dropping off. It's also one that the family will enjoy.

225 g (8 oz) ready-to-eat mixed fruit,
  i.e. figs, mango, pear, prunes,
  chopped
125 g (4½ oz) blanched almonds,
  chopped
450 g (1 lb) strong flour
1 teaspoon salt
75 g (2¾ oz) soft brown sugar
grated zest of 1 lemon
1 packet dried yeast
250 ml (9 fl oz) skimmed milk, warmed
50 g (1¾ oz) butter, melted
1 egg, beaten

1 Mix together the mixed fruit, almonds, flour, salt, sugar, lemon zest and yeast.

2 Make a well in the centre and pour in the warm milk and melted butter.

3 Mix to a soft dough. Turn the dough out of the bowl and knead for 10 minutes.

4 Return the dough to the bowl and cover with cling film or a damp cloth.

5 Leave to rise in a warm place for about 2 hours until it has doubled in size.

6 'Knock back' the risen dough and shape it to fit a 1 kg/2 lb loaf tin.

7 Cover with cling film and a damp cloth and leave to rise again for a further 2 hours.

8 Preheat the oven to Gas Mark 4/180°C/350°F. Brush the top of the loaf with beaten egg.

9 Bake for 20 minutes, then cover with foil and bake for a further 30 minutes. It's ready when the base sounds hollow when tapped.

10 Remove from the tin and leave to cool.

 **Fruit Cake**

Ⓥ

3 Points per serving

78½ Total Points per recipe

205 Calories per serving

㉔ Servings

Freezing recommended. Preparation time: 20 minutes + 2 hours baking.

This recipe contains no eggs, which helps keep Points low. It is very light and, don't worry, you can't taste the vinegar!

225 g (8 oz) reduced-fat spread,
  e.g. Krona
450 g (1 lb) plain flour
450 g (1 lb) mixed dried fruit
225 g (8 oz) soft brown sugar
1 teaspoon bicarbonate of soda
300 ml (½ pint) skimmed milk
3 tablespoons malt vinegar

1 Preheat the oven to Gas Mark 6/200°C/400°F.

2 Line a 25 cm (10-inch) cake tin with greaseproof paper.

3 Rub the reduced-fat spread into the flour and add the fruit and sugar.

4 Sprinkle the bicarbonate of soda into the milk and then add the vinegar. It will foam and, while still frothing, add it to the dry ingredients and mix well.

5 Turn into the cake tin and bake for 30 minutes. Reduce the oven temperature to Gas Mark 3/170°C/320°F and bake for a further 1½ hours.

6 Leave to cool in the tin for 30 minutes, then turn on to a wire rack to cool completely.

Cranberry Muffins

Cook's tips

The bicarbonate of soda and vinegar act as the raising agent, and so must be added to the mixture while still foaming.

It is often easier to cut up the cake neatly if you use a square tin.

Ⓥ

3 Points per muffin

35 Total Points per recipe

170 Calories per muffin

⑫ Muffins

Freezing recommended. Preparation and cooking time: 1 hour.

These have a lovely Christmassy flavour.

100 g (3½ oz) plain flour
100 g (3½ oz) wholemeal flour
3 teaspoons baking powder
½ teaspoon ground cinnamon
75 g (2¾ oz) soft brown sugar
75 g (2¾ oz) butter, melted
1 egg, lightly beaten
125 ml (4 fl oz) runny low-fat yogurt
125 ml (4 fl oz) skimmed milk
100 g (3½ oz) dried cranberries

1 Put 12 muffin cases into a muffin tin. Preheat the oven to Gas Mark 6/200°C/ 400°F.

2 Sieve flours together and add the baking powder, cinnamon and sugar.

3 Mix the butter, egg, yogurt and milk together. Stir into the dry ingredients and add cranberries.

4 Fill the muffin cases with the mixture.

5 Bake for 20–25 minutes until risen and golden brown.

Cranberry Muffins

Oat and Apple Cake

V

1 Point per square

20 Total Points per recipe

80 Calories per square

16 Squares

Freezing recommended. Preparation and cooking time: 45 minutes.

This is a cake with a lovely flavour.

100 g (3½ oz) wholemeal flour

1 teaspoon ground ginger

50 g (1¾ oz) soft margarine

50 g (1¾ oz) rolled oats

50 g (1¾ oz) soft brown sugar

125 ml (4 fl oz) skimmed milk

2 eating apples, peeled and sliced

2 tablespoons jelly marmalade,

1 Lightly grease an 18 cm (7-inch) square tin. Preheat the oven to Gas Mark 5/190°C/375°F.

2 Sieve together the flour and ginger. Rub in the margarine.

3 Mix in the rolled oats and sugar. Mix to a soft dropping consistency with the milk and spread this mixture evenly into the tin.

4 Arrange the apple slices over the top of the mixture. Brush with melted jelly marmalade.

5 Bake for 25–30 minutes.

6 Mark into 16 squares, but leave to cool before serving.

 Easter Biscuits

V

2 Points per biscuit

25½ Total Points per recipe

135 Calories per biscuit

12 Biscuits

Freezing recommended. Preparation and cooking time: 30 minutes.

These spicy crunchy biscuits are a lovely treat at any time of the year.

100 g (3½ oz) low-fat spread

75 g (2¾ oz) caster sugar + extra for

* sprinkling*

1 egg, separated

200 g (7 oz) plain flour

1 teaspoon mixed spice

50 g (1¾ oz) currants

2 tablespoons skimmed milk

1 Preheat the oven to Gas Mark 6/200°C/ 400°F. Lightly grease two baking sheets.

2 Cream together the margarine and sugar, beat in the egg yolk.

3 Sieve together the flour and mixed spice and stir into the creamed mixture.

4 Add the currants and milk to form a soft dough.

5 Knead lightly on a floured surface and roll out thinly.

6 Cut into rounds using a 7.5 cm (3-inch) cutter. Re-roll where necessary.

7 Put on baking trays and bake for 8 minutes. Remove from the oven and brush with the egg white, sprinkle with a little caster sugar and return to the oven for a further 3 minutes until golden brown.

8 Cool on a wire rack.

 **Crispy Cakes**

V

1½ Points per square

12 Total Points per recipe

75 Calories per square

9 Squares

Freezing not recommended. Preparation and cooking time: 10 minutes.

These are very popular with children. You could also make them in bun cases; petit-fours cases are good for little children's parties.

15 g (½ oz) margarine

4 tablespoons golden syrup

1 tablespoon sugar

75 g (2¾ oz) Rice Krispies

1 Melt the margarine and syrup. Add the sugar.

2 Mix in the Rice Krispies and press firmly into an 18 cm (7-inch) tin.

3 Cool and cut into squares.

Coconut Kisses

V

2½ Points per cake
40½ Total Points per recipe
90 Calories per cake
16 Cakes

Freezing not recommended. Preparation time: 15 minutes + 2–3 hours baking. These are deliciously light and so simple to make.

3 medium egg whites, beaten stiffly
125 g (4½ oz) caster sugar
150 g (5½ oz) desiccated coconut
1 teaspoon ground semolina

1 Preheat the oven to Gas Mark 2/150°C/ 300°F.
2 When the egg whites are stiff enough to stand up in soft peaks, lightly stir in the other ingredients, using a large metal spoon.
3 Line a baking sheet with non-stick baking paper. Drop spoonfuls of the mixture on to the baking sheet and bake for 2–3 hours until crisp and lightly coloured.

Cook's tip
When whisking egg whites, always ensure that they are at room temperature, and that both bowl and beater are clean and dry.

Variation
Add just a drop of red food colouring to one half of the mixture to give a rosy pink tinge to half your coconut kisses.

Chocolate-iced Fairy Cakes

V

1½ Points per cake
19 Total Points per recipe
90 Calories per cake
12 Cakes

Freezing not recommended. Preparation time: 15 minutes + 12 minutes baking. These take very little time and trouble, and because they're low in Points, you can afford to indulge yourself over a cuppa.

225 g packet McDougalls Low-Fat
*   Sponge Mix*
1 medium egg
125 ml (4 fl oz) water
For the icing
2 tablespoons icing sugar, sieved
2 teaspoons cocoa powder
a little warm water

1 Preheat the oven to Gas Mark 6/200°C/ 400°F.
2 Put the sponge mix into a bowl. Add the egg and 4 dessertspoons of water. Mix well, and then beat for 2 minutes until smooth.
3 Add the rest of the water and beat for a further minute. Spoon into paper cake cases which you have placed on a baking sheet.
4 Bake for 10–12 minutes until lightly golden and firm to the touch.
5 Cool, and when ready to ice, mix the sieved icing sugar and cocoa powder to a paste with a few drops of warm water.
6 Ice the cakes and leave to set.

Cook's tip
These can be made using ready-bought fairy cakes, but they will be higher in Points.

Variation
Omit the cocoa powder and add a drop of red or yellow food colouring to the icing.

French Glazed Strawberry Tarts

1½ Points per tart
5½ Total Points per recipe
80 Calories per tart
4 Tarts

Freezing not recommended. Preparation time: 10 minutes + 15 minutes baking. These should be eaten as soon as possible after baking since the pastry is so light that it will go soggy after a couple of hours.

2 sheets Jus-Rol filo pastry from a 270 g pack, defrosted
1 tablespoon polyunsaturated margarine, melted
4 tablespoons low-fat ready-to-serve custard
225 g (8 oz) strawberries, halved
1 dessertspoon redcurrant jelly, warmed

1 Brush 1 sheet of the pastry with half the melted margarine.
2 Lay the other sheet on top and brush with the rest of the margarine.
3 Cut your double layer of pastry into 4 and use to line a 4-hole non-stick Yorkshire pudding tin. Bake for 12–15 minutes until crisp and golden.
4 Cool and fill with the low-fat custard and strawberries.
5 Brush the top of each with warmed redcurrant jelly to glaze, and eat while fresh.

Cook's tips
Return the rest of the pastry to the freezer as soon as possible after defrosting.
   If you don't have a 4-hole Yorkshire pudding pan, bake the pastry (in one piece) in an ordinary non-stick sponge or flan tin. This won't fit exactly, so you'll have to trim the edges.

Weight Watchers tip
Filo pastry is very light, low in Points, and consequently ideal for Weight Watchers Members. However, it is also very fragile and needs careful handling – so read the pack instructions carefully.

Variation
Use raspberries instead of strawberries.

French Glazed Strawberry Tarts

Crunchy Apple and Blackberry Tartlets

Ⓥ

1 Point per tartlet
14 Total Points per recipe
85 Calories per tartlet
12 Tartlets

Freezing not recommended. Preparation time: 10 minutes + 10 minutes baking. These are very quick, light and low in Points. So go ahead – spoil yourself!

1 tablespoon polyunsaturated margarine, melted
12 slices low-calorie bread
2 teaspoons caster sugar
½ teaspoon ground cinnamon
375 g can Bramley Apple and Blackberry Pie Filling

1 Preheat the oven to Gas Mark 6/200°C/400°F.
2 Brush each hole of a 12-hole bun or muffin tin with a little margarine.
3 Cut out 12 circles of bread, using a 7 cm (3-inch) pastry cutter, or a tumbler.
4 Line each section of the tin with a circle of bread.
5 Mix the remainder of the margarine with the caster sugar and cinnamon and use to brush the circles of bread.
6 Bake for 8–10 minutes until crisp and golden.
7 Allow to cool before filling with the apple and blackberry mixture.

Variation
Use a cherry pie filling.

Buttermilk Pancakes

Ⓥ

1 Point per pancake
8½ Total Points per recipe
45 Calories per pancake
12 Pancakes

Freezing recommended. Preparation time: 5 minutes + 25 minutes cooking. These American-style pancakes are just the thing for breakfast, lunch or supper with a savoury filling, or simply to enjoy at teatime.

1 egg white
100 g (3½ oz) + 1 tablespoon self-raising flour
a pinch of salt
300 ml (½ pint) buttermilk
low-fat cooking spray

1 Beat the egg white until it stands up in soft peaks.
2 Sift the flour and salt into a bowl and make a well in the centre.
3 Add about a third of the buttermilk and beat till smooth.
4 Beat in the rest of the milk, and then gently mix in the egg white using a large metal spoon.
5 Heat a small non-stick frying pan over a medium heat, and when hot spray a couple of times with low-fat cooking spray.
6 Drop 1 tablespoonful of pancake batter into the pan and tilt it so that it spreads evenly over the base. Cook for a minute or so until it begins to set and bubbles appear on the surface. Flip over and cook the other side.

7 Cook the rest of the pancakes the same way, stacking them between sheets of greaseproof or non-stick baking paper as they come out of the pan, and spraying with cooking spray when necessary. Serve hot or cold.

Cook's tips
Serve with fruit canned in natural juice and a dollop of diet yogurt or low-fat fromage frais, adding the extra Points.

For a savoury meal, fill with seafood and top with a low-fat cheese sauce, adding the extra Points.

Weight Watchers tip
Buttermilk is much lower in fat than semi-skimmed milk, and is obtainable from most major supermarkets. If you can't get it, use semi-skimmed or skimmed milk. If you choose skimmed, use a whole egg instead of just the white, or the mixture will be very bland. Calories per pancake would then be 50 and Points would be the same.

Rich Fruit Christmas Cake

Ⓥ

4 Points per slice

90 Total Points per recipe

250 Calories per slice

㉔ Slices (each weighing around 75 g/2¾ oz)

Freezing not recommended. Preparation time: 25 minutes + 2½–3 hours baking. Rich, moist and bursting with fruit, this cake is low in saturated fats because it's made with corn oil rather than butter. The ingredients list is rather long, but they all add to the taste, and it's very simple to make. A 16-year-old schoolgirl, making a Christmas cake for the first time, tested the recipe for us, and it turned out brilliantly!

125 ml (4 fl oz) corn oil
175 g (6 oz) soft dark brown sugar
3 eggs
450 g (1 lb) mixed dried fruit
100 g (3½ oz) glacé cherries, halved
225 g (8 oz) wholemeal flour, sieved
1 teaspoon baking powder
1 teaspoon mixed spice
2 tablespoons brandy or rum
a little skimmed milk (optional)

For the icing

3 egg whites
450 g (1 lb) icing sugar, sieved
1 tablespoon lemon juice

1 Preheat the oven to Gas Mark 3/170°C/320°F.

2 Beat the corn oil, sugar and eggs together in a large bowl.

3 Stir in the dried fruit and cherries.

4 Sieve the flour again with the baking powder and mixed spice. Stir gently but thoroughly into the fruit mixture, using a large metal spoon.

5 Add the brandy or rum and, if necessary, a little skimmed milk to give a soft 'dropping' consistency.

6 Lightly oil a 20 cm (8-inch) round tin, and line with a double thickness of baking parchment. Spoon the mixture into the tin and bake for 2½–3 hours. It is ready when a skewer comes out clean.

7 Leave to cool for about 1 hour before turning out on to a wire rack.

8 When cold, wrap in a double layer of foil and leave for at least 48 hours, (or up to 4 weeks), before icing.

9 To ice: lightly beat the egg whites and mix with the sieved icing sugar and lemon juice until thick and smooth. Spread over the cake using a spatula (or a round-bladed knife) dipped in hot water. The hot water enables the icing to spread more evenly.

Cook's tips

Egg whites should always be beaten at room temperature, not straight from the fridge. If they are too cold, they won't whisk properly. Also, make sure that both bowl and beater are clean and dry.

Weight Watchers tip

If you like marzipan on your Christmas cake, you can buy some ready made from most supermarkets. Be warned, however, that it's fiendishly high in both Calories and fat. Adjust the Points if you use it.

Crunchy Fruit Fingers **Page 187**
Rich Fruit Christmas Cake

 ## Crunchy Nutty Choccie Bites

ⓥ

1 Point per bite

11 Total Points per recipe

55 Calories per bite

⓬ Bites

Freezing not recommended. Preparation time: 10 minutes + minimum 2 hours chilling.

These are child's play to make. There's no cooking involved, and kids and adults love them!

25 g (1 oz) icing sugar, sieved
1 tablespoon cocoa powder
25 g (1 oz) low-fat spread
100 g (3½ oz) Jordan's Original Crunchy
  Cereal with Raisins and Almonds

1 Mix the icing sugar, cocoa powder and low-fat spread with 2 teaspoons of water.
2 Put the cereal in a bowl, stir in the icing sugar/cocoa mixture and mix thoroughly.
3 Spoon into paper cake cases and chill for 2 hours or overnight.

 ## Choccie Crisp Cookies

ⓥ

½ Point per cookie

26 Total Points per recipe

35 Calories per cookie

㊵ Cookies

Freezing not recommended. Preparation time: 15 minutes + 15 minutes baking.

These little American-style cookies are very moreish, but they're also low in Points, so you can afford to indulge yourself when you feel like a treat!

50 g (1½ oz) polyunsaturated margarine
100 g (3½ oz) caster sugar
2 eggs + 1 egg white
125 g (4½ oz) plain flour, sieved
1 tablespoon cocoa powder
½ teaspoon bicarbonate of soda
25 g (1 oz) dark chocolate, grated
  coarsely

1 Beat the margarine and sugar together until soft and creamy.
2 Beat the 2 eggs in a bowl and in a separate bowl beat the egg white. Fold them together using a large metal spoon.
3 Mix together the sieved flour, cocoa powder and bicarbonate of soda.
4 Add the egg mixture to the creamed sugar and margarine a little at a time, adding spoonfuls of flour in between, and mixing lightly but thoroughly.
5 Mix in the grated chocolate.
6 Line a baking sheet with non-stick baking paper. Spoon heaped teaspoonfuls of the mixture on to the baking tray; flatten the mixture slightly with the bowl of the spoon.
7 Bake for 10–15 minutes or until lightly browned and beginning to firm up.
8 Cool on a wire rack and store in an airtight container.

Crunchy Fruit Fingers

V

1 Point per finger

27½ Total Points per recipe

75 Calories per finger

20 Fingers

Freezing not recommended. Preparation time: 15 minutes + 20 minutes baking. These are like cereal bars but much, much nicer, and so easy to make.

50 g (1¾ oz) polyunsaturated margarine
100 g (3½ oz) malt extract
100 g (3½ oz) stoned dates, chopped
*   finely*
100 g (3½ oz) ready-to-eat stoned
*   prunes, chopped finely*
200 g (7 oz) rolled oats

1 Preheat the oven to Gas Mark 4/180°C/ 350°F.
2 Melt the margarine in a small pan and stir in the malt extract.
3 Add the dates, prunes and rolled oats and stir until well-combined.
4 Spread evenly in a shallow, non-stick baking tray and bake for 20 minutes or until golden and just beginning to firm up.
5 Remove from the oven, mark into fingers and leave in the tin to cool.
6 When completely cold and firm, cut into fingers and store in an airtight container.

Cook's tip
This is an excellent recipe for children to make.

Variation
Substitute ready-to-eat dried apricots or apples for the prunes or dates. Whichever you choose, they'll be equally healthy.

Prepared the starter, the main course is cooking away happily, there's just dessert to think about. Let Weight Watchers do all the thinking for you – just flick through the recipes in this chapter. All the treats you'll find here are dead easy to make. Many of them put ready-made ingredients to good use, for example our Strawberry Tarts use petticoat tail shortbread and fromage frais, and the Kiwi Castles are a decorative way to serve ready-made low-sugar jelly with fruit.

There are recipes here for the cheesecake lover (try Mini Raspberry Cheesecakes), and for the addict of lovely traditional fruit puds and custard. Our speedy Fruit Crumble is a simple concoction of fresh bananas and canned pineapple with a crunchy crumble topping. Serve with some low-fat custard. See? You can have your cake and eat it!

desserts

Fruit Crumble

Ⓥ

4½ Points per serving

28 Total Points per recipe

285 Calories per serving

6 Servings

Freezing recommended. Preparation time: 10 minutes + 35 minutes cooking. Crumbles are usually high in fat because the topping uses the same amount of butter or margarine as pastry. Ready-made crumble toppings are great time-savers, and in this recipe, a ready-made topping is mixed with a fruity muesli to keep the Points down. To save you having to peel, chop and stew fruit, this dish uses fresh bananas and a can of pineapple.

2 large bananas, sliced thinly
225 g (8 oz) canned pineapple rings
    in fruit juice, cut into pieces, juice
    reserved
225 g (8 oz) packet crumble mix
100 g (3½ oz) unsweetened wholewheat
    muesli with dried fruit

1 Preheat the oven to Gas Mark 5/190°C/375°F. Lightly grease an ovenproof dish.
2 Layer the bananas and the pineapple with the juice in the dish.
3 Mix the crumble with the muesli and spread this mixture over the fruit.
4 Bake for 30–35 minutes until golden brown. Serve hot or cold.

Variation
Canned peaches or soaked dried apricots also go well with the bananas.

Pears in Hot Chocolate Sauce

Ⓥ

1 Point per serving

6 Total Points per recipe

70 Calories per serving

5 Servings

Freezing not recommended. Preparation and cooking time: 10 minutes.

410 g canned pear halves in natural
    juice, drained
cocoa powder for dusting

For the custard sauce
300 ml (½ pint) skimmed milk
2 teaspoons sugar
2 teaspoons cocoa powder
2 teaspoons custard powder

1 Make up the custard sauce with the skimmed milk and sugar according to the packet instructions, adding the cocoa powder with the custard powder.
2 Place the pear halves upside-down on a serving dish.
3 Pour the hot sauce over the pears, dust with a little cocoa powder and serve immediately.

Variation
This can also be served chilled.

Marshmallow and Chocolate Fool

3 Points per serving

14½ Total Points per recipe

175 Calories per serving

5 Servings

Freezing not recommended. Preparation time: 15 minutes + chilling.

50 g sachet Asda less-than-10%-sugar
    Delight
300 ml (½ pint) skimmed milk
40 g (1½ oz) mini marshmallows
500 g carton low-fat ready-to-serve
    custard

1 Make up the Delight with the skimmed milk according to the packet instructions. Mix in most of the marshmallows, saving some for decoration.
2 Layer about 3 dessertspoons of the custard into individual serving dishes. Cover this with a thin layer of the Delight (about 2 dessertspoonfuls).
3 Repeat the layers, finishing with the Delight and decorate the top with the remaining marshmallows. Chill before serving.

Weight Watchers tip
Delight mixes vary in fat and Calories. This one from Asda is a little lower in fat than regular versions.

Black Grape and Banana Trifle

5 Points per serving

19 Total Points per recipe

145 Calories per serving

4 Servings

Freezing not recommended. Preparation time: 15 minutes + chilling.

8 sponge fingers

50 ml (2 fl oz) unsweetened orange juice

1 large banana, sliced thinly

2 Rowntrees individual ready-to-eat low-sugar jellies, cut into cubes

4 tablespoons aerosol cream

16 seedless black grapes, halved

For the custard

1 tablespoon custard powder

1 tablespoon sugar

300 ml (½ pint) skimmed milk

1 Make up the custard using the sugar and skimmed milk according to the packet instructions. Chill in the refrigerator.

2 Take four individual sundae dishes. Put 2 sponge fingers in each dish (you may need to cut them in half). Pour the orange juice over them.

3 Layer the banana slices on top and immediately cover with the jelly cubes.

4 Spread the thick, cooled custard over the jelly.

5 Give each trifle a squirt of aerosol cream just before serving and decorate with the grapes.

Black Grape and Banana Trifle

 **Peach Crisp**

2 Points per serving

11 Total Points per recipe

120 Calories per serving

5 Servings

Freezing not recommended. Preparation time: 15 minutes + chilling.

49 g pack no-added-sugar peach flavour Angel Delight
300 ml (½ pint) skimmed milk
410 g can peach halves in fruit juice, drained on kitchen paper
5 tablespoons crushed cornflakes

1 Make up the Angel Delight using the skimmed milk, according to the packet instructions.
2 Cut each peach half into bite-sized pieces. Put a layer of peach pieces in individual sundae dishes.
3 Spread the Delight over the peaches and allow to chill in the refrigerator.
4 Before serving, sprinkle the cornflakes on top.

Cook's tip
It's best not to prepare this dish too much in advance, since the Delight will start to separate.

 **Creamy Apricot Rice**

V

2 Points per serving

8 Total Points per recipe

105 Calories per serving

4 Servings

Freezing not recommended. Preparation and cooking time: 10 minutes.
Ever made a rice pud from scratch? It takes ages in the oven, so why not try this speedy recipe? It uses a can of low-fat rice pudding flavoured with nutmeg and apricots.

25 g (1 oz) ready-to eat apricots, chopped into bite-sized pieces
a pinch of nutmeg
1–2 drops vanilla essence (optional)
2 tablespoons raisins
425 g can Weight Watchers from Heinz rice pudding

1 Put all the ingredients into a pan and heat thoroughly until the fruits are soft. Serve hot or cold.

Raspberries Layered with Crème Fraîche and Filo Pastry

5½ Points per serving

10½ Total Points per recipe

390 Calories per serving

2 Servings

Freezing not recommended. Preparation and cooking time: 20 minutes.
This is a simple recipe for that special occasion à deux, but it's also very simple to double up for a dinner party.

8 sheets filo pastry
125 g (4½ oz) half-fat crème fraîche
125 g (4½ oz) fresh raspberries
a dusting of icing sugar

1 Preheat the oven to Gas Mark 4/180°C/ 350°F.
2 Cut 8 circles of filo pastry 10 cm (4 inches) in diameter.
3 Place on a baking sheet lined with baking parchment and lightly dust with icing sugar. Bake for 4–5 minutes or until golden brown.
4 Allow the circles to cool and then take a circle and top with a generous spoonful of crème fraîche and a few raspberries.
5 Top with another circle and crème fraîche and raspberries. Repeat with another layer of ingredients. Top with a final circle and lightly dust with icing sugar. Make another dessert in the same way.
6 If any raspberries remain, purée and pour a little around each dessert.

Greek Yogurt and Honey

Ⓥ

1½ Points per serving

40 Calories per serving

❶ Serving

Freezing not recommended. Preparation time: 5 minutes.

If you've ever travelled to the Greek islands, you'll remember this popular dessert, often quite sticky and great to round off a rich meal. Greek yogurt contains around 10% fat, so this recipe mixes it with low-fat plain yogurt – all the taste but less on your waist!

1 dessertspoon Greek-style natural yogurt, chilled
1 dessertspoon low-fat plain yogurt, chilled
1 teaspoon runny honey
1 teaspoon chopped nuts

1 Mix both the yogurts together and place in a serving bowl.
2 Swirl the honey over this and sprinkle with the chopped nuts. Serve immediately.

 ### Yogurt with Passion

Ⓥ

2½ Points per serving

5 Total Points per recipe

120 Calories per serving

❷ Servings

Freezing not recommended. Preparation time: 10 minutes.

2 × 125 ml pots low-fat plain yogurt
1 small red apple, chopped
10 green seedless grapes, halved
2 teaspoons runny honey
1 passion fruit, seeds and pulp only

1 Mix the yogurt with the apple and grapes.
2 Swirl the honey over the top and scatter with passion fruit seeds.

 ### Ginger and Ice Crunch

Ⓥ

2½ Points per serving

110 Calories per serving

❶ Serving

Freezing not recommended. Preparation time: 5 minutes.

1 ginger nut biscuit
1 scoop Weight Watchers Ice Cream
1 ice cream wafer

1 Break the biscuit into small pieces.
2 Either mix with the ice cream in a bowl, or put the ice cream in a dish and decorate with the biscuits.
3 Top with the wafer and serve immediately.

Ginger and Ice Crunch
Pears in Hot Chocolate Sauce **Page 190**

Mandarin and Chocolate Dream

3 Points per serving

110 Calories per serving

1 Serving

Freezing not recommended. Preparation time: 5 minutes.

1 Weight Watchers from Heinz Chocolate Mousse

8 canned mandarins or 1 fresh mandarin, peeled and segmented

4 white chocolate drops

1 Put a little less than half the mousse in a glass bowl and top with 4 mandarin slices.

2 Repeat with the same quantity of mousse and the remaining mandarin segments. Finish with the remaining mousse. Decorate with white chocolate drops.

Cook's tip

If white chocolate drops are not available use milk chocolate, or use 2 white chocolate buttons, halved.

Hot Fruity Bananas

V

2 Points per serving

7 Total Points per recipe

110 Calories per serving

4 Servings

Freezing not recommended. Preparation time: 5 minutes + 20 minutes cooking.

4 medium bananas

2 tablespoons unsweetened orange juice

25 g (1 oz) dried mixed peel, chopped

4 dessertspoons fromage frais, to serve

1 Preheat the oven to Gas Mark 7/220°C/425°F. Make a lengthways slit in each banana, taking care that the skin doesn't peel off.

2 Pour the juice into each slit.

3 Sprinkle each banana with the dried peel and wrap them in kitchen foil to make 4 parcels.

4 Bake these banana parcels until soft (about 15–20 minutes). Serve with a spoonful of fromage frais.

Hot Fruity Bananas
Mandarin and Chocolate Dream

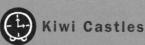

Mini Pavlova

V

3 Points per serving
175 Calories per serving
1 Serving

Freezing not recommended. Preparation time: 5 minutes.

1 bought mini-meringue nest
1 scoop Weight Watchers Ice Cream
1 fresh peach, sliced

1 Fill the meringue with the ice cream.
2 Top with peach slices.

Mini Pavlova

Kiwi Castles

1½ Points per serving
6 Total Points per recipe
75 Calories per serving
4 Servings

Freezing not recommended. Preparation time: 10 minutes.
Having difficulty entertaining the children? Get them to help out with this fun dessert (yummy for adults too).

475 g pack of 4 individual Rowntrees
low-sugar jellies
100 ml (3½ fl oz) light evaporated milk
4 kiwi fruits, peeled and sliced

1 Invert the jellies on to individual serving plates.
2 Pour a 'sea' of 3 tablespoons of evaporated milk around each jelly.
3 Place one slice of kiwi on top of each 'castle'.
4 Cut the remaining slices in half and arrange these 'islands' decoratively in the sea.

Christmas Pudding

V

3½ Points per serving
43½ Total Points per recipe
250 Calories per serving
12 Servings

Freezing not recommended. Preparation time: 20 minutes + overnight soaking + 4 hours cooking.

No suet? No flour? And you can make a Christmas pudding? The answer is – Yes! Try it and see. It's rich, dark, delectable and low in Points. Don't be afraid of the long list of ingredients – just mix them all together, give them a good stir, and you're well on the way!

275 g (9½ oz) fresh wholemeal
*   breadcrumbs*
500 g pack Whitworth's mixed fruit
125 g pack ready-to-eat dried prunes
2 tablespoons cut mixed peel
225 g (8 oz) Bramley apple, peeled,
*   cored and grated finely*
1 carrot, peeled and grated finely
1 teaspoon mixed spice
½ teaspoon ground cinnamon
1 tablespoon coarse-cut marmalade
juice and zest of 1 orange
3 medium eggs
2 tablespoons dark treacle
4 tablespoons brandy or rum
150 ml (¼ pint) port or sherry

1 Put the breadcrumbs, fruit, carrot and spices into a large bowl and mix thoroughly.

2 In another bowl put the marmalade, orange juice and zest, eggs, treacle, brandy or rum and port or sherry and beat until well blended.

3 Pour over the dry ingredients, stir until well blended and leave to soak overnight to let the flavour of the spices develop.

4 Lightly oil a 1.2-litre (2-pint) pudding basin and spoon in the mixture, packing it quite tightly.

5 Oil a large square of greaseproof paper and tie firmly over the top.

6 Put the bowl in a large saucepan and add enough water to come halfway up the side of the bowl. Once the water is gently simmering steam the pudding for 4 hours, making sure that the level of the water is kept topped up.

7 When pudding is cooked, allow it to cool in the pan. Remove from the pan and wrap the pudding – bowl and all – in a double layer of foil.

8 Steam for 2 hours, as described in step 6, before serving.

Cook's tip
The pudding can be cooked much quicker in a microwave or pressure cooker. Timings vary a lot so read the manufacturer's instructions.

 ## Tangy Oranges

V

1 Point per serving
3½ Total Points per recipe
90 Calories per serving
4 Servings

Freezing not recommended. Preparation time: 15 minutes + chilling.
This simple recipe can be served on its own or with low-fat fromage frais. Remember to adjust the Points.

4 oranges, peeled and sliced
1 tablespoon sugar
2 tablespoons unsweetened orange juice
juice of 1 lemon

1 Put the sliced oranges in a dish and sprinkle with the sugar.

2 Pour the orange juice and the lemon juice over the oranges.

3 Mix gently and put them in the fridge to chill.

Knickerbocker Glory

Ⓥ

2 Points per serving

9 Total Points per recipe

110 Calories per serving

4 Servings

Freezing not recommended. Preparation time: 10 minutes.

A favourite with the whole family; the classic 'naughty-but-nice' end to any meal.

225 g (8 oz) fresh or canned
strawberries
juice of 2 oranges
4 scoops Weight Watchers Vanilla
Iced Dessert
4 glacé cherries
4 wafers

1 Liquidise or mash the strawberries and add to the orange juice.

2 Mix the ice cream with the strawberries, until you have a smooth texture.

3 Serve immediately topped with a glacé cherry. Accompany with the wafers.

Variation

You could serve the orange/strawberry mixture and the ice cream in layers in a tall stemmed glass.

Christmas Peaches

Ⓥ

1 Point per serving

4 Total Points per recipe

40 Calories per serving

4 Servings

Freezing not recommended. Preparation time: 5 minutes + 10 minutes cooking.

Christmas Peaches make a lighter alternative to Christmas pudding, and they're ideal for Boxing Day when you don't want to do much cooking.

410 g canned peach halves in natural
juice, drained
4 teaspoons dried mixed fruit
4 teaspoons brandy (optional)

1 Preheat the oven to Gas Mark 7/220°C/420°F.

2 Put 4 peach halves, hollow-side up, in a non-stick bun tray.

3 Put 1 teaspoon of dried mixed fruit in the hollow of each peach.

4 Pour 1 teaspoon of brandy, if using, over the dried fruit in each peach. If you don't want to use brandy, use some of the peach juice instead.

5 Heat for 10 minutes and serve.

Cook's tip

Using a non-stick bun tray prevents the peaches from falling over, but any ovenproof dish will do.

Crunchy Yogurt Delight

Ⓥ

2 Points per serving

8½ Total Points per recipe

120 Calories per serving

4 Servings

Freezing not recommended. Preparation time: 10 minutes.

A speedy, low-fat, high-fibre dessert.

300 ml (½ pint) low-fat plain yogurt
2 tablespoons clear honey
75 g (2¾ oz) muesli with no added sugar

1 Mix the honey with the yogurt.

2 Sprinkle generously with muesli.

Variation

Substitute drained canned peaches for the muesli. Calories per serving will be 80.

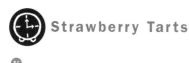 **Strawberry Tarts**

V

2 Points per serving

9 Total Points per recipe

90 Calories per serving

4 Servings

Freezing not recommended. Preparation time: 10 minutes.

Whoever would have thought that a tempting strawberry tart could be part of a weight-watching plan? Well in just 10 minutes you can create this mouth-watering dish to indulge on your own, or to impress those party guests.

3 tablespoons half-fat crème fraîche
4 shortbread petticoat tails
225 g (8 oz) strawberries, halved

1 Spread the crème fraîche on the petticoat tails and cover with the strawberries.

Weight Watchers tip

Shortbread is high in fat, but this is a treat which compares well with other desserts.

Variations

Try ginger nuts with fresh or canned mandarins, orange segments or kiwi fruit slices. Reduce Points by ½ per serving. Calories per serving will be 60.

 **Festive Pudding**

V

1½ Points per serving

6½ Total Points per recipe

145 Calories per serving

4 Servings

Freezing not recommended. Preparation time: 20 minutes + 20 minutes cooking. A warming pudding for a cold night and a hint of brandy to give it the Christmas touch.

450 g (1 lb) apples, peeled and sliced
25 g (1 oz) sultanas
½ teaspoon cinnamon
2 teaspoons sugar
For the brandy custard sauce
300 ml (½ pint) skimmed milk
2 teaspoons sugar
1 tablespoon brandy
2 teaspoons custard powder

1 Make up the custard sauce with the skimmed milk and sugar according to the packet instructions, adding the brandy with the custard powder.
2 Cook the apples and sultanas in a little water in a saucepan until they are soft but still holding their shape.
3 Place in the bottom of a non-stick, ovenproof dish. Pour over the brandy custard sauce.
4 Mix the sugar and cinnamon together and sprinkle over the top.
5 Bake for 20 minutes at Gas Mark 6/200°C/400°F.

 Mini Raspberry Cheesecakes

2½ Points per serving

10½ Total Points per recipe

155 Calories per serving

4 Servings

Freezing recommended. Preparation time: 30 minutes + minimum 2 hours chilling. These make a lovely dinner party dessert, and your guests need never know that you're trying to lose weight.

50 g (1¾ oz) reduced-fat digestive biscuits
25 g (1 oz) low-fat spread
175 g (6 oz) raspberries, fresh or frozen without added sugar and defrosted
100 g (3½ oz) diet cottage cheese, sieved
150 g carton low-fat raspberry yogurt
2 teaspoons powdered gelatine
2 teaspoons granulated sweetener

1 Using a rolling pin crush the digestive biscuits between 2 sheets of greaseproof or non-stick baking paper. Melt the low-fat spread and mix into the biscuit crumbs.
2 Press the mixture into the bottom of 4 ramekin dishes, and put in the fridge to chill while preparing the topping.
3 Save 4 whole raspberries for decoration. Mix the sieved cottage cheese with the rest of the raspberries (which will be crushed as you mix them), and combine with the raspberry yogurt.
4 Sprinkle the gelatine on to 2 tablespoons water in a teacup. Stand the cup in a pan of hot water. Stir until the gelatine is completely dissolved, and then

gently mix into the raspberry mixture.

5 Stir in the granulated sweetener. Spoon the mixture into the ramekins on top of the biscuit mix. Decorate each with a whole raspberry and chill for at least 2 hours.

Variation

Use crushed strawberries in place of raspberries.

Fruit Flan

v

2 Points per serving

7 Total Points per recipe

105 Calories per serving

4 Servings

Freezing not recommended. Preparation time: 15 minutes + chilling.

A colourful array of fresh fruits on top of a creamy citrus filling make this a refreshing dessert which is rich in vitamin C.

2 tablespoons orange juice

2 tablespoons low-fat plain fromage frais

75 g medium flan case

2 peaches, sliced

2 kiwi fruits, sliced

1 strawberry

1 Mix the orange juice with the fromage frais and spread the mixture into the flan case.

2 Decorate with fruit and serve chilled.

Fruit Flan

Raspberry Rice

Ⓥ

1½ Points per serving

6 Total Points per recipe

90 Calories per serving

4 Servings

Freezing not recommended. Preparation time: 10 minutes.
A quick dessert, highly suitable if you are on holiday and self catering.

200 g (7 oz) fresh raspberries
400 g (14 oz) can Weight Watchers
*   from Heinz rice pudding*

1   Reserve 4 raspberries for the top. Take 4 tall glasses and place a few fresh raspberries in the bottom.
2   Top with some of the rice pudding. Repeat, finishing with the rest of the rice and top with a raspberry.

Raspberry Rice

Black Forest Roll

6 Points per serving

24½ Total Points per recipe

195 Calories per serving

8 Servings

Freezing recommended. Preparation and cooking time: 25 minutes.
A very simple but effective dessert. A little of your favourite liqueur could make it a little more special, but do remember to count the Points.

3 eggs
75 g (2¾ oz) caster sugar + extra for
*   sprinkling*
50 g (1¾ oz) self-raising flour
25 g (1 oz) cocoa powder
400 g (14 oz) can black cherry pie filling
125 g (4½ oz) half-fat crème fraîche,
*   to serve*

1   Grease and line with baking parchment a swiss roll tin 23 cm × 33 cm (9 × 13 inches). Preheat the oven to Gas Mark 7/220°C/425°F.
2   Whisk together the eggs and caster sugar until very thick and creamy. This may take 5 minutes with an electric mixer.
3   Sieve in the flour and cocoa. Mix well and pour into the tin. Bake in the middle of the oven for 8 minutes, until lightly brown and springy.
4   Lay a sheet of greaseproof paper on top of a damp tea towel. Sprinkle caster sugar on to the paper.
5   Turn out the sponge cake and roll up with greaseproof paper inside. Allow to cool.
6   Carefully unroll the sponge cake.
7   Spread the pie filling over the sponge cake and gently roll up.
8   Serve with the crème fraîche.